The
St. Martin's
WORKBOOK
for Canadians

The

St. Martin's

WORKBOOK

for Canadians

Lex Runciman
Oregon State University

Frances Peck
Consultant

Nelson Canada

© Nelson Canada
A Division of Thomson Canada Limited, 1992
1120 Birchmount Road
Scarborough, Ontario
M1K 5G4

Excerpt (page 127): from *The Coming of Winter* by David Adams Richards. Copyright © 1974 by David Adams Richards. Reprinted by permission of Oberon Press.

Canadian Cataloguing in Publication Data
Runciman, Lex
    The St. Martin's workbook for Canadians

Supplement to: Lunsford, Andrea A., 1942–   . The
St. Martin's handbook for Canadians.
ISBN 0-17-604143-5

1. English language—Grammar—Problems, exercises,
etc. 2. English language—Rhetoric—Problems,
exercises, etc. 3. Report writing—Problems,
exercises, etc. I, Peck, Frances. II. Lunsford,
Andrea A., 1942–   . The St. Martin's handbook
for Canadians. III. Title.

PE1112.L82 1992   428.2   C91–094374–5

Printed and bound in Canada
1 2 3 4   WC   95 94 93 92

OTABIND

Bound to stay open

The pages in this book open easily and lie flat, a result of the Otabind bookbinding process. Otabind combines advanced adhesive technology and a free-floating cover to achieve books that last longer and are bound to stay open.

CONTENTS

P A R T   I V

Making Sentence-Level Choices: Grammar

PART IV   PREVIEW QUESTIONS

These questions are designed to help you, the student, decide what you need to study. Read each sentence and underline the word or words specified in parentheses or underline the correct word of the two provided within the sentence. (Answers to preview questions are found at the back of the book.)

1. Meryl drove her car to the supermarket. (nouns)
2. The McCraes brought their pet to the doctor. (nouns)
3. Makiko will get a new dress after she finishes her exams. (verbs)
4. Richard might speak to his father about going to the ball game. (verbs)
5. Anybody could buy Prince's record, but only those who went downtown could buy his new single. (pronouns)
6. Which restaurant do you want to go to? (pronouns)
7. Until nine o'clock she waited under the bridge, but then she gave up and walked away. (prepositions)
8. Celia and (I, me) are very close friends.
9. The audience did not know (who, whom) to applaud.
10. (Who, Whom) did you call this morning?
11. Both (he, him) and (her, she) were chosen for the play.
12. They invited both John and (I, me) to the party.
13. I (is, am) a marvelous cook.
14. That woman (don't, doesn't) want anyone to help her.
15. Sarah (gives, gave) John a piece of candy yesterday.
16. John (lay, lied) on the bed until he felt better.
17. If I had done better (will, would) you be satisifed?
18. Neither I nor anyone else (want, wants) trouble.
19. The class assembled at (its, their) usual time.
20. Each student should bring (his, a) notebook to class.
21. My family (travel, travels) to India tonight.

1

22. The members of my family (has, have) much in common.
23. The news (is, are) always on at six o'clock.
24. She began to feel (good, well) after a few days.
25. Dave was the (more, most) handsome of the three.
26. He wrote a (real, really) hard exam.
27. Marianne is (more nice, nicer) than her brother, but her father is the (nicest, nicer) of all of them.

On a separate sheet of paper, list at least one of each of the following, taken from any of the sentences above: a complete subject, a complete predicate, a direct object, an indirect object, a possessive pronoun, a linking verb, a past tense verb, a future tense verb, and a compound subject. Check your answers against the material presented in the next five chapters; if you need help, ask your instructor.

— 13 —
Constructing Grammatical Sentences

EXERCISE 13.1 IDENTIFYING VERBS

Underline the verbs or verb phrases in the following sentences.

1. The clock on the wall reads 2:15.
2. The cleaners will be finished with your coat on Friday.
3. Alice, you must tell me before tomorrow.
4. That mug on his desk has not been washed in three weeks!
5. Grosbeaks make a distinctive sound.
6. I will always choose broccoli over asparagus.
7. Music lifts my spirits.

EXERCISE 13.2 IDENTIFYING NOUNS

Underline all the nouns in these sentences.

EXAMPLE

    The soprano strode onto the stage.

1. For an hour, Leonard chopped wood.
2. Marcia wore dark glasses.
3. Angie and Harry drove for three hours on the highway.
4. The quiche served at The Valley tastes delicious.
5. A dog grows extra hair to prepare for winter.
6. *Sports Illustrated* featured an article on Mike Tyson.
7. My mother's chocolate chip cookies always tasted great.

EXERCISE 13.3 IDENTIFYING PRONOUNS

Underline all the pronouns in the following sentences. The first sentence has been done for you.

1. That cup, which you found on the coffee table, is mine.
2. Our assignment is due Wednesday.
3. Louis noticed that his lawn was full of dandelions.
4. Most of us enjoy a good movie occasionally.
5. Her superiors praised her work for the environmental committee.
6. Everyone who is fascinated by cities should see New York.
7. The plover that we sighted yesterday has its nest on Boughton Island.

EXERCISE 13.4   IDENTIFYING ADJECTIVES

On a separate sheet of paper, compose six adjective-noun pairs. Underline each adjective you use.

EXERCISE 13.5   IDENTIFYING ADVERBS

Choosing from the following list, add adverbs to sentences 2–7 in Exercise 13.1. Write your new sentences out on a separate sheet of paper. The adverbs to choose from are *early, promptly, really, almost, thoroughly, willingly, usually, always,* and *gladly.* Feel free to use others if you prefer. Sentence 1 from Exercise 13.1 has been done for you below.

EXAMPLE

The clock on the wall *clearly* reads 2:15.

EXERCISE 13.6   IDENTIFYING PREPOSITIONAL PHRASES

Underline the prepositional phrases in the following sentences. The first sentence has been done for you.

1. We finally purchased the light bulbs for that lamp.
2. I'll meet you in the hotel lobby after work.
3. After a meal of turkey, potatoes, and creamed onions, I had no room for dessert.
4. With the exception of my chemistry class, I'm having a good term.
5. With so many blouses in stock, we should probably have a sale.
6. The computer ribbons for your Panasonic printer arrived in the latest shipment.
7. Contestants for the poetry prize should mail their entries before April 1.

EXERCISE 13.7   IDENTIFYING CONJUNCTIONS AND INTERJECTIONS

Read the following sentences. Underline conjunctions once and interjections twice. The first sentence has been completed for you.

1. Hey! Even though I'm little, I still want to go with you.
2. Before you order dessert, make sure you have enough money to cover it.
3. After breakfast, either I'll rake the leaves or I'll go for a walk.
4. Ouch! That grade wasn't what I'd anticipated.
5. Jake and Sandy, Elly and André, and Louise and Michael all plan to travel together and attend the conference.
6. Dee is arranging her schedule so that she can chair next week's meeting.
7. Our parts shipment did not arrive yesterday, so I cannot fill your order.

EXERCISE 13.8   IDENTIFYING SUBJECTS AND PREDICATES

In each sentence, underline the subject once and the predicate twice.

EXAMPLE

Life is just a bowl of cherries.

1. His coffee tasted too strong.
2. The phonograph needle skips every time.
3. That telephone has rung constantly all morning.
4. April rains have refilled the reservoirs.
5. The fishing season opens soon.
6. The typewriter ribbon was fixed last night.
7. Her letter answers every question.

EXERCISE 13.9   IDENTIFYING AND USING DIRECT AND INDIRECT OBJECTS

Read the following sentences. Underline each direct object once and each indirect object twice. If a sentence has no direct or no indirect object, leave the sentence as is. The first sentence has been done for you.

1. Jerry poured his coffee into a flamingo pink cup.
2. After dinner, we went to the store for oranges and a loaf of bread.
3. The candidate delivered an impassioned speech.
4. Digital technology gives listeners almost flawless sound.
5. The flicker landed in the tree and sang to us.
6. You should give Mrs. Zanefeld a copy of your poem.
7. Mr. Chudczak called the principal over the intercom.

Using the following verbs, construct pairs of sentences, one using an indirect object and one converting that indirect object to the object of a preposition.

EXAMPLE

   Verb: sent

   a. *indir. obj.* The president sent his secretary a memo.
   b. *obj. of prep.* The president sent a memo to his secretary.

8. Verb: gave

a. *indir. obj.* _____

_____

b. *obj. of prep.* _____

_____

9. Verb: threw

a. *indir. obj.* _____

_____

b. *obj. of prep.* _____

_____

10. Verb: handed

a. *indir. obj.* _____

_____

b. *obj. of prep.* _____

_____

EXERCISE 13.10   USING PREPOSITIONAL PHRASES

Add a prepositional phrase to each of the following sentences. Circle the phrase you add, use an arrow to indicate the word your phrase modifies, and indicate whether the phrase functions as an adjective or an adverb.

EXAMPLE

Carrie slept.

(After dinner,) Carrie slept.   Phrase functions as an adverb.

1. Sanjay felt ill. _____

_____

2. Her speech convinced me. _____

_____

3. The barn is a local landmark. _____

_____

4. The plumbers will repair that leak. _____

_____

5. Carole announced that she was leaving. _____

_____

EXERCISE 13.11   USING INFINITIVES, GERUNDS, AND PARTICIPLES

Add the specified phrase to the given sentence.

EXAMPLE

I discovered the book _____. (Add the past participle of *hide* to modify *book*.)
I discovered the book hidden under the couch.

1. Joan enjoyed _____. (Add the gerund form of *run* to complete the sentence.)

2. _____, I arrived just as class began. (Add a present participial phrase modifying the subject *I*.)

3. Alan tried _____. (Add an infinitive phrase to complete the sentence.)

4. _____, you should count calories and exercise regularly. (Add an infinitive phrase.)

5. _____, it is a good idea _____. (Add two infinitive phrases.)

6. Our family has always enjoyed _____. (Add a gerund phrase.)

7. _____, the house needed a lot of work. (Add a past participial phrase.)

EXERCISE 13.12   IDENTIFYING DEPENDENT CLAUSES

Read the following passage and underline the dependent clauses. The first dependent clause has been underlined for you.

Dick and I remember that afternoon well. The sun glinted off the ocean as we pulled into the provincial park. Dick said that the surf looked a little high. Even so, we weren't worried. After we were seated in the kayak and headed into the waves, we began getting worried. Each wave washing over us put us lower in the water. Before we had time to think, we found ourselves underwater. It was quiet and pale blue under there. When we struggled to shore half an hour later, a man who had been watching strolled over to us. I'll never forget what he said. "Well, you made it, though for a while there I wasn't sure that you would."

EXERCISE 13.13   UNDERSTANDING FUNCTION AND FORM

Underline each independent clause in the sentences that follow. Then identify each sentence according to function and form.

EXAMPLE

Will you take me to the store when I get home from school?
Function: interrogative
Form: complex

1. Either you take me to the store, or I'll run away!

   Function: _____

   Form: _____

2. Although we received considerable precipitation during April, the drought is not over.

   Function: _____

   Form: _____

3. Is it true that Lake Park Roller Rink has been closed?

   Function: _____

   Form: _____

4. While we were sleeping, Alec went to the store for us, and he has even fixed us dinner!

   Function: _____

   Form: _____

5. I can still taste the delicious Cajun chicken that you prepared for us last night.

   Function: _____

   Form: _____

ASSIGNMENT 13A   IDENTIFYING THE PARTS OF SPEECH

Identify the part of speech of each underlined word as it functions in the sentence.

EXAMPLE

> The car door slammed into the utility pole.
> car: adjective   door: noun   into: preposition

1. The car sped down Main Street and barely missed two pedestrians.

   _____

   _____

2. You should have read two chapters before tomorrow's class.

   _____

   _____

3. As the Mississippi winds south toward the delta, it grows and widens and becomes something awesome, magical, even terrifying.

   _____

   _____

4. Yes, Moncton, New Brunswick, did receive over ten inches of snow on April 27.

   _____

   _____

5. That particular essay question gave everyone trouble.

   _____

   _____

ASSIGNMENT 13B   USING LINKING VERBS AND SUBJECT COMPLEMENTS

With the subjects provided, construct sentences using linking verbs followed by predicate adjectives.

EXAMPLE

> cup
> The cup was broken.

1. lights _____

   _____

2. sweater _____

_____

3. ocean _____

_____

4. perfume _____

_____

5. painting _____

_____

Using the subjects provided, construct sentences using linking verbs followed by predicate nouns. The predicate nouns may be modified by adjectives.

EXAMPLE

sand wedge
A sand wedge is a golf club.

6. this car _____

_____

7. that track star _____

_____

8. a piano _____

_____

9. those buildings _____

_____

10. two celebrities _____

_____

ASSIGNMENT 13C   UNDERSTANDING LINKING, TRANSITIVE, AND INTRANSITIVE VERBS

The following sentences give a subject and a verb. Complete each sentence by adding an indirect object and a direct object. Underline the direct object once and the indirect object twice.

EXAMPLE

The school sent Mary her grades.

1. Beth handed _____.

2. The dog brought _____.

3. Charlie passed _____.

4. Sally threw _____.

5. Music gave _____ .

Identify the underlined verb in each sentence as either transitive, intransitive, or linking.

EXAMPLE

The race started with a pistol shot. intransitive
This fettucine tastes divine. linking
You should wear a coat today. transitive

6. These fossilized clams are twenty-five million years old. _____

7. Mingo Construction erected that chain-link fence. _____

8. My supervisor has requested a copy of your report. _____

9. Out on the lake, the loon called for a long time. _____

10. The Taylors' cat seems sick today. _____

ASSIGNMENT 13D USING PHRASES

Combine or add to the following sentences as specified.

EXAMPLE

Harold phoned Monica. (Add infinitive phrase.)
Harold phoned Monica to ask her for a date.

1. Monica called Harold. (Add only a prepositional phrase.)

   _____

2. Harold called to cancel their date. (Add a present participial phrase).

   _____

3. Nippers Harbour, L'Anse au Loup, and Little Burnt Bay were all named after bodies of water. All these communities can be found in Newfoundland. (Combine using a past participial phrase.)

   _____

   _____

4. Thomas Chandler Haliburton established himself as an important 19th-century Canadian writer. He was also a provincial court judge. (Combine using an appositive phrase.)

   _____

   _____

5. Lisa likes to swim every other morning. It keeps her fit. (Combine using a gerund phrase as the subject.)

   _____

   _____

6. You should watch your diet and exercise regularly. (Add an infinitive phrase.)

_____

_____

7. Test the water. (Add a prepositional phrase with a gerund functioning as the object of the preposition.)

_____

_____

8. The warehouse burned fiercely. (Add a present participial phrase.)

_____

_____

9. Colin James is a rock and blues singer. He is gaining a national reputation. He will appear in concert next week. (Combine using an appositive phrase that contains a present participial phrase.)

_____

_____

10. My ears were ringing and my hands were aching. I left the concert and headed for my car. (Combine using an absolute phrase.)

_____

_____

ASSIGNMENT 13E USING CLAUSES

Determine whether each clause is independent or dependent. Then add a clause of your own.

EXAMPLES

When lightning hit the roof   (Make into a complex sentence.)
(dependent clause)   Every bulb in the place blew out when lightning hit the roof.

the alarm sounded   (Make into a compound sentence.)
(independent clause)   The burglar shattered the window, and the alarm sounded.

1. before you decide   (Make into a complex sentence.)

_____

2. Bruce caught the ball on the run   (Make into a compound sentence.)

_____

3. the candy had disappeared   (Make into a complex sentence.)

_____

4. the class that you suggested   (Make into a complex sentence.)

_____

5. when Horowitz appeared   (Make into a compound-complex sentence.)

   _____

6. a gentle wind stirred the yard   (Make into a compound sentence.)

   _____

7. the abandoned car was covered with rust   (Make into a complex sentence.)

   _____

8. after we'd finished dinner   (Make into a compound-complex sentence.)

   _____

9. the paper was nowhere to be found   (Make into a compound sentence using any co-ordinating conjunction except *and*.)

   _____

10. she closed the file drawer   (Make into a complex sentence.)

   _____

Select six of the ten sentences you have just written (all declarative sentences). Convert two of them to interrogative sentences, two to imperative sentences, and two to exclamatory sentences. You may shorten your original sentences to single dependent clauses.

EXAMPLE

   The burglar shattered the window, and the alarm sounded. (declarative sentence)
   Tell me what time the burglar shattered the window. (imperative sentence)

11. interrogative sentence:

   _____

12. interrogative sentence:

   _____

13. imperative sentence:

   _____

14. imperative sentence:

   _____

15. exclamatory sentence:

   _____

16. exclamatory sentence:

   _____

— 14 —

Understanding Pronoun Case

EXERCISE 14.1 USING SUBJECTIVE CASE PRONOUNS

Read each of the following sentences, replacing the underlined noun or nouns with the appropriate subjective case pronoun. Then copy each sentence, including the pronoun you have selected, on a separate sheet of paper. As you write each sentence, ask yourself whether the pronoun sounds right to you. If it does not sound right, reread section 14a of the handbook and consider whether you have chosen the correct pronoun.

EXAMPLE

Jack and George visited the zoo.
Jack and I visited the zoo.

1. Whenever Kim, David, and Sean visited the beach, the weather was bad.
2. As the cattle crossed the road, the cattle stopped all traffic.
3. Chris was a better tennis player than Al.
4. The rhododendrons are most beautiful in May when the rhododendrons bloom.
5. Jody, Susan, Scott, and I were the only people still in the building.
6. Tom wondered if Tom was smarter than James.
7. Allison was curious to see whether or not Allison would be asked to work late.
8. Symphonies are popular, but not all cities have symphonies.
9. The cars slowed to a stop whenever the cars approached an on-ramp.
10. Dick, Brad, and I have a great time whenever Dick, Brad, and I get together.

EXERCISE 14.2 USING PRONOUNS TO DISTINGUISH BETWEEN GERUNDS AND PARTICIPLES

Identify the underlined word as either a gerund or a participle. Be able to explain the different meanings and constructions for each pair of sentences.

1. a. We saw their signalling clearly.
   b. We saw them signalling clearly.
2. a. We heard them singing without regard for our comfort.
   b. We heard their singing without regard for our comfort.
3. a. We watched his tightrope walking cautiously.
   b. We watched him tightrope walking cautiously.

EXERCISE 14.3 USING WHO AND WHOM TO BEGIN QUESTIONS

Underline the correct pronoun in each of the following sentences.

1. Who/Whom did you consult before purchasing the car?
2. Who/Whom took that wonderful photograph?
3. Who/Whom should receive first prize?
4. Who/Whom was the Sweet Marie candy bar named after?
5. Who/Whom was the first to run a mile in less than four minutes?

EXERCISE 14.4 USING *WHO, WHOM, WHOEVER*, AND *WHOMEVER* TO BEGIN
DEPENDENT CLAUSES

Work through the following four sentences to determine whether to use a subjective or an objective
relative pronoun.

EXAMPLES

    She identified the clerk who had given her the wrong change.
    The subordinate clause by itself is _____ had given her the wrong change.
    Inserting a personal pronoun (he/she/him/her/they/them) yields he had given her the wrong change
    Does this personal pronoun act as the subject or as an object? subject
    Thus, the correct relative pronoun in this sentence is who.

    At the party, Alice talked to whomever she found interesting.
    The subordinate clause by itself is _____ she found interesting (or, in a more normal word
    order, she found _____ interesting).
    Inserting a personal pronoun (he/she/him/her/they/them) yields she found them interesting.
    Does this personal pronoun act as the subject or as an object? object
    Thus, the correct relative pronoun in this sentence is whomever.

1. Jack said he would be glad to speak to _____ showed up to listen.

    The subordinate clause by itself is _____

    _____.

    Inserting a personal pronoun (he/she/him/her/they/them) yields

    _____.

    Does this personal pronoun act as the subject or as an object? _____.

    Thus, the correct relative pronoun in this sentence is _____.

2. She shared the secret with those _____ she trusted.

    The subordinate clause by itself is _____

    _____.

    Inserting a personal pronoun (he/she/him/her/they/them) yields

    _____.

    Does this personal pronoun act as the subject or as an object? _____.

    Thus, the correct relative pronoun in this sentence is _____.

3. _____ he instructed to write this brief certainly did not do a thorough job.

The subordinate clause by itself is _____

_____.

Inserting a personal pronoun (he/she/him/her/they/them) yields

_____

Does this personal pronoun act as the subject or as an object? _____.

Thus, the correct relative pronoun in this sentence is _____.

4. Today's weather forecast should please anyone _____ enjoys skiing on fresh powder.

The subordinate clause by itself is _____

_____

Inserting a personal pronoun (he/she/him/her/they/them) yields

_____

Does this personal pronoun act as the subject or as an object? _____.

Thus, the correct relative pronoun in this sentence is _____.

ASSIGNMENT 14A USING OBJECTIVE CASE PRONOUNS

Several of the following nine sentences use objective case pronouns incorrectly. Identify the incorrect sentences, and rewrite them in correct form. If the sentence is already correct, place a *C* on the line below the sentence.

EXAMPLE

Whenever we order a drink, the bartender asks we for a drink.
Whenever we order a drink, the bartender asks us for a drink.

1. With a long week behind we, a brisk Saturday walk gives Sonja and I some much needed exercise.

_____

_____

2. When Pam finished dinner, Julie reminded she to study physics.

_____

3. Charlie asked her to give he a call later.

_____

4. Eventually the headwaiter told Kim, Sidney, and I that we could be seated.

_____

5. After three days of steady rain, gale force winds toppled several trees and left they looking like huge, spilled matchsticks.

_____

_____

6. For Bill, Monty, and I, running 25 kilometres a day was our training for the marathon.

_____

7. Before we could say anything more, Amy loaned Oscar and I thirty dollars.

_____

8. Though even the idea of hang-gliding made her nervous, she gave it a try.

_____

9. Tony called she before him left the house.

_____

ASSIGNMENT 14B USING SUBJECTIVE, OBJECTIVE, AND POSSESSIVE CASE PRONOUNS

Substitute pronouns for the nouns shown in parentheses after each blank.

EXAMPLE

They (Jerry and David) drove their (Jerry and David's) own car to the convention so that they (Jerry and David) would not have to rent one.

1. _____ (Ron's) sleeping late made _____ (Diane and me) late for our first class.

2. _____ (The ducks') arriving so early will mean some of _____ (the ducks) may starve.

3. While Linda carries the baby, would you mind carrying _____ (Linda's) suitcase?

4. _____ (Brent) asked _____ (Brent) if _____ (Brent) had made the right decision.

5. Whether _____ (Carrie) goes or whether _____ (Carrie) stays, _____ (Nathan's) love for _____ (Carrie) doesn't change, nor does _____ (Carrie's) love for _____ (Nathan).

ASSIGNMENT 14C USING WHO, WHOM, WHOEVER AND WHOMEVER

Underline the correct pronoun choice in each of the following sentences and briefly explain the reason for your choice.

EXAMPLE

The woman who/whom I met is, I discovered today, the sales manager.
Whom functions as the object of the verb met.

1. The government officials to who/whom we were referred have refused to see us.

   _____

2. Whoever/Whomever informed you of the test location made a mistake.

   _____

3. Who/Whom should we notify in case of illness?

   _____

4. I was contacted by the officials who/whom you describe.

   _____

5. The salesperson who/whom Dad called is here to speak with whoever/whomever is interested in buying the new vacuum cleaner.

   _____

6. Who/Whom called this salesperson?

   _____

7. The client who/whom phoned you earlier is on the line again now.

   _____

8. People who/whom do not vote have no cause to complain.

   _____

ASSIGNMENT 14D USING CORRECT PRONOUN CASE WITH APPOSITIVES

In each of the following sentences, determine which pronoun form should be used. Write the entire correct sentence on the lines provided.

1. City life is what we/us Torontonians thrive on.

   _____

2. For we/us Nova Scotians, history is everywhere.

   _____

3. For two Newfoundlanders, she/her and Bernie, the flatness of Saskatchewan came as quite a shock. _____

   _____

4. As newcomers Dale and I/me found out, Sudbury has a long history of mining. _____

   _____

5. Lute Johannson always claimed he was the best of us/we chili cookers. _____

   _____

6. There is only one whiskey to we/us real Scots.

   _____

7. Two Irish writers, she/her and William Butler Yeats, must share the title of best writer.

   _____

8. The committee gave the two finest storytellers, Ed and I/me, citations of merit.

   _____

9. That country house looked good to we/us longtime apartment dwellers.

   _____

10. Even to Les and he/him, the computer eventually proved to be a powerful tool.

    _____

— 15 —

Using Verbs

EXERCISE 15.1 USING AUXILIARY VERBS

Underline the auxiliary and main verb in each sentence below. If an incorrect auxiliary has been used, pencil in the correct auxiliary above it. If a needed auxiliary has been left out, pencil it in. If the sentence is correct, write *C* next to the number of the sentence.

EXAMPLE

                  is

    Grandma <u>were feeling</u> better this morning.

1. I is running for the position of class president.
2. After careful study, we inclined to accept the consultant's report.
3. Whenever Veronica misses school, you can bet she has developed another ear infection.
4. Since Ravi has been reading Robert Louis Stevenson, he don't watch much television.
5. When the alarm bell rings, we must leave the building immediately.

EXERCISE 15.2 DISTINGUISHING BETWEEN *LIE/LAY*, *SIT/SET*, AND *RISE/RAISE*

Underline the correct verb in each of the following sentences. The first one is done for you.

1. Alice sat/<u>set</u> her cup of tea on the drainboard.
2. After a strenuous tennis match, Dave only wanted to set/sit in an easy chair.
3. The cat had lain/laid there so long that it was stiff when it stood up.
4. Lee couldn't remember where he'd sat/set his glass.
5. The class began to fidget because they had sat/set so long.
6. If we lie/lay the wrench here, will we remember to put it away?
7. Where is the chicken that lain/laid the golden egg?
8. I'm going to lie/lay down.
9. I'm going to lie/lay myself down.
10. Lois sat/set down at her sewing machine and sat/set the material out in front of her.
11. As the flag was rose/raised, the children sang "O Canada."
12. The dough bubbles as it raises/rises.

EXERCISE 15.3 USING VERB TENSES IN SEQUENCES

Read the following sentences carefully, and provide the specified information. If a sentence uses a logical sequence of tenses, put *L* on the lines provided. If the sentence uses an illogical sequence of tenses, rewrite it so that your new version is logical. You may find that you need to review the sections in the handbook that identify the various tenses.

EXAMPLE

Crowfoot Hunter threw a curve even though the catcher will signal a fast ball.
main verb: <u>threw</u>
tense of main verb: <u>past</u>
dependent clause verb: <u>will signal</u>
tense of dependent clause verb: <u>future</u>
Crowfoot Hunter threw a curve even though the catcher signalled a fast ball.

1. Liz Claiborne had designed dresses before she designs eyewear and other accessories.

   main verb: _____

   tense of main verb: _____

   dependent clause verb: _____

   tense of dependent clause verb: _____

   _____

   _____

2. Dad's gift was a shirt that proved too small.

   main verb: _____

   tense of main verb: _____

   dependent clause verb: _____

   tense of dependent clause verb: _____

   _____

   _____

3. Mom will have left by the time you arrive.

   main verb: _____

   tense of main verb: _____

   dependent clause verb: _____

   tense of dependent clause verb: _____

   _____

   _____

4. The light had just changed to green when the pickup truck crumples the passenger side of my Volkswagen.

   main verb: _____

   tense of main verb: _____

   dependent clause verb: _____

tense of dependent clause verb: _____

_____

_____

5. The soap opera had just started when our power will go out.

main verb: _____

tense of main verb: _____

dependent clause verb: _____

tense of dependent clause verb: _____

_____

_____

EXERCISE 15.4 IDENTIFYING ACTIVE AND PASSIVE VOICE

Underline the verb in each sentence, and indicate whether it is active or passive.

EXAMPLE

The azalea blossoms nod in the wind. active.

1. The next section of this report analyses the experimental data. _____

2. The experimental data are analysed in the next section of this report. _____

3. Suddenly, rainfall pounded on the roof over our heads. _____

4. The last apple fritter in the doughnut box was eaten by Jerry just a few minutes ago. _____

5. By this time tomorrow afternoon, they will be fishing for trout. _____

6. The wall clock downstairs says 8:05. _____

7. My paper was put in your mailbox yesterday afternoon after lunch. _____

8. My roommate put my paper in your mailbox yesterday afternoon after lunch. _____

9. Erica's purse had been returned to the lost and found. _____

10. A variety of factors contributed to the outbreak of the First World War. _____

EXERCISE 15.5 IDENTIFYING VERB MOODS

Read the following short paragraph from a letter. Above each underlined verb, pencil in the mood of that verb. The first verb mood has been identified for you.

Dear Brenda and Dan,

    indicative

We were pleased by your suggestion that we meet for several days at Cavendish Beach this year, and if the

distance from Montreal to the coast were even 300 kilometres less, such a trip to the beach would be feasible for us. Unfortunately, given the actual distance (and the fact that our motor home <u>needs</u> repair), we'll simply not be able to make the trip this summer. But <u>ask</u> the Harringtons. They <u>moved</u> to Kingston only last year. We <u>thought</u> of them because Bill Harrington always <u>speaks</u> of his love of beachcombing. Besides, Bill and Sue <u>are</u> a wonderful couple. <u>Keep</u> us posted on your plans. If we <u>were planning</u> any trip this summer, it would be to see you both.

EXERCISE 15.6   USING VERB MOODS

Using your own paper, write accurate, original sentences using the mood and verb specified. Remember, the subjunctive commonly appears in clauses beginning with *if, that, as if,* or *as though.*

EXAMPLES

a sentence using the verb *bark* in the indicative mood
<u>Whenever another dog walks by, our Tom barks.</u>

a sentence in which the verb *ask* is followed by a subjunctive
<u>The personnel manager asks that you be interviewed tomorrow.</u>

1. a sentence using *carry* in the imperative mood
2. a sentence in which the verb *insist* is followed by a subjunctive
3. a sentence in which the verb *wish* is followed by a subjunctive
4. a sentence using *climb* in the indicative mood
5. a sentence using *call* in the imperative mood

ASSIGNMENT 15A   USING VERB FORMS

Using the subjects and verbs provided, write the indicated sentences.

EXAMPLE

subject: *Bernie*   verb: *touch*
sentence using a present form: <u>Bernie touches the soft fur.</u>
sentence using the auxiliary verb *had*: <u>Bernie had touched a squid before.</u>

1. subject: *I*   verb: *walk*   sentence using a past form: _____

_____

sentence using an auxiliary verb + the present participle form: _____

_____

2. subject: *they*   verb: *ask*   sentence using a present form: _____

_____

sentence using an auxiliary verb + the past participle form: _____

_____

3. subject: *the birds*   verb: *screech*   sentence using a past form: _____

_____

sentence using an auxiliary verb + the present participle form: _____

_____

4. subject: *we*   verb: *decide*   sentence using a present form: _____

_____

sentence using the auxiliary verb *had* + the past participle form: _____

_____

5. subject: *teenagers*   verb: *consume*   sentence using a past form: _____

_____

sentence using the auxiliary verb *were* + the present participle form: _____

_____

ASSIGNMENT 15B   USING IRREGULAR VERBS

Consulting the list of irregular verbs in the handbook, write sentences as specified. Use auxiliary verbs as needed.

EXAMPLE

a sentence using *they* as its main subject and the past participle form of *go* as its main verb (Remember that past participle forms are combined with auxiliary verbs.)
By the time we arrived, they had gone for supplies.

1. a sentence using *we* as its subject and the past tense form of *think* as its main verb

_____

2. a sentence using *they* as its main subject and the past form of *bring* as its main verb

_____

3. a sentence using any personal name as its main subject and the past participle form of *become* as

its main verb _____

_____

4. a sentence using *circus* as its main subject and the past participle form of *begin* as its main

verb _____

_____

5. a sentence using *I* as its main subject and the past participle form of *forget* as its main verb

_____

6. a sentence using *we* as its main subject and the past form of *draw* as its main verb

_____

7. a sentence using any appropriate noun as its subject and the past form of *drink* as its main verb _____

8. a sentence using *they* as its subject and the past participle form of *feel* as its main verb

_____

9. a sentence using any appropriate noun as its subject and the past participle form of *freeze* as its main verb _____

_____

10. a sentence using *I* as its main subject and the past participle form of *pass* as its main verb

_____

ASSIGNMENT 15C USING THE PRESENT TENSES

For each specified verb and tense, write a sentence. If the verb is irregular, you may need to consult the list of irregular verbs in the handbook or a good dictionary.

EXAMPLE

run present perfect
The new car has run every day without fail.

1. *climb*, present progressive _____

_____

2. *marry*, present perfect progressive _____

_____

3. *discuss*, present _____

_____

4. *begin*, present progressive _____

_____

5. *tease*, present perfect _____

_____

6. *devour*, present _____

_____

7. *confuse*, present perfect progressive _____

_____

24

8. *lie* (tell an untruth), present progressive _____

_____

9. *sit*, present perfect _____

_____

ASSIGNMENT 15D USING THE PAST TENSES

For each specified verb and tense, write a sentence. If the verb is irregular, you may need to consult the list of irregular verbs in the handbook or a good dictionary.

EXAMPLE

swim, past perfect progressive
I had been swimming for years before the injury.

1. *ride*, simple past _____

_____

2. *drink*, past perfect _____

_____

3. *steal*, past perfect _____

_____

4. *walk*, past perfect progressive _____

_____

5. *protest*, past progressive _____

_____

6. *require*, simple past _____

_____

7. *enjoy*, past perfect progressive _____

_____

8. *drive*, past progressive _____

_____

9. *sleep*, past perfect _____

_____

10. *delight*, simple past _____

_____

ASSIGNMENT 15E   USING THE FUTURE TENSES

For each specified verb and tense, write a sentence. If the verb is irregular, you may need to consult the list of irregular verbs in the handbook or a good dictionary.

EXAMPLE

> *swim* future perfect
> You will have swum thirty laps by the time I wake up.

1. *decide*, future progressive _____

   _____

2. *remember*, future _____

   _____

3. *compose*, future perfect _____

   _____

4. *fly*, future perfect progressive _____

   _____

5. *fish*, future progressive _____

   _____

6. *visit*, future perfect progressive _____

   _____

7. *consult*, future perfect _____

   _____

8. *oppose*, future _____

   _____

9. *hike*, future perfect _____

   _____

10. *celebrate*, future progressive _____

    _____

ASSIGNMENT 15F   USING VERB TENSES IN LOGICAL SEQUENCE

Read each sentence below. If the sequence of tenses is logical, place an *L* on the first line following the sentence. If the sequence of tenses is illogical, rewrite the sentence on the lines that follow.

EXAMPLE

> When the family cat got hungry, she decides to climb the window screen and look inside.
> When the family cat got hungry, she decided to climb the window screen and look inside.

1. I had just finished spading the garden when you come out with the cold drinks.

    _____

2. On the first sunny Saturday in April, we decided to have taken a hike.

    _____

3. Surprised by winning the lottery, she decided to take a week off.

    _____

4. Before we started to have eaten dinner, we emptied the dishwasher.

    _____

5. The committee needs to have met for an extra hour next week.

    _____

6. The evergreens began to grow where the meadow grass ended.

    _____

7. They announced the winners after we will finish dessert.

    _____

8. Mark had just stepped out of the shower when the lights started to have flickered.

    _____

9. Anita has surgery last month and hopes to begin training again next week.

    _____

10. Some Canadian historians would love to live in 1867.

    _____

— 16 —

Maintaining Agreement

EXERCISE 16.1 MAINTAINING SUBJECT-VERB AGREEMENT

Read the following paragraph. Then go back and look at each sentence. Circle the sentence subject and underline the main verb. (Ignore dependent clauses.) If the sentence subject and verb do not agree, pencil in the accurate verb. The first sentence has been done for you. (*Hint*: Remember that sentence subjects cannot be the objects of prepositions.)

consists

(Saguenay Park,) situated near Chicoutimi, Quebec, <u>consist</u> of nearly 300 square kilometres of land on both sides of the Saguenay River. One of the park's most striking features are the Saguenay fjord. Created during the Ice Age by glaciers that gouged through the Laurentians to the St. Lawrence River, the fjord today make a dramatic sight for nature-lovers. Visitors sometimes spots whales, which are native to the fjord. Naturalists at the park's Visitor Centre describes the park's wildlife in more detail and explains how the fjord was formed. In addition to the fjord, there is many paths for hikers. The trails wind through the forested valley, which hugs either side of the river. One of the trails lead to the top of cap Trinité. At the summit, a statue of the Virgin Mary stands 183 metres above the river. Such dramatic sights makes Saguenay Park well worth a visit.

EXERCISE 16.2 MAKING VERBS AGREE WITH RELATIVE PRONOUN SUBJECTS

Underline the correct verb form in each of the following sentences. In each case, you should be able to explain your choice.

EXAMPLE

   Tom is one of those dogs that <u>bark</u>/barks at bees or cars or the neighbour's radio. [*Many dogs bark: Tom is just one of them.*]

1. Weeks that is/are as rainy as this one make me sleepy.
2. She will ask one of the students who arrive/arrives early to help her distribute the new assignment.
3. The Gary Larson cartoons that you like/likes are posted on the bulletin board.
4. The mayor says that decisions that affect/affects us all should be decided by the city council rather than by the city administrators.
5. One of the contestants who enter/enters will win a trip for two to Key West, Florida.

EXERCISE 16.3   CHECKING SUBJECT-VERB AGREEMENT

Assume that the following paragraph is taken from a persuasive essay. Read the paragraph carefully, and underline the verbs. If a verb does not agree with its subject, cross out the verb and write the correct form above it. You may need to review earlier sections of this chapter. The first two verbs have been underlined for you.

Besides harming their own bodies, smokers also <u>endanger</u> the good health of people around them. Cigarette smoke, either from a smoker's exhalation or straight from the cigarette, <u>contain</u> carbon monoxide, a highly poisonous gas. Nobody appreciate breathing in poisonous gas. And it is not just the health factors that keeps people away from smokers. Even nonsmokers who do not know about carbon monoxide is usually bothered by the smoke because it makes breathing difficult. In addition, a lot of smoke in closed rooms are often irritating to the eyes. Many people is also disgusted when they smells a smoker's clothes or sees the yellow nicotine stains on a smoker's front teeth. Finally, not too many people enjoy kissing somebody whose mouth taste like an ashtray.

EXERCISE 16.4   MAINTAINING ACCURATE AGREEMENT

Write a paragraph (or more) that describes your ideal dinner menu. Make sure that your final version includes discussion of at least three courses of food (main course, salad, and dessert, for example). Make readers taste, see, and smell the food you describe. Try to make their mouths water.

Use your own paper for the paragraph. When you have written it, make a list showing all subjects and their verbs and all pronouns and their antecedents for each of the first five sentences of your paragraph. Make sure that all of your subjects agree with their verbs and that all of your pronouns agree with their antecedents. If any disagree, correct them.

SAMPLE OPENING SENTENCE

My ideal dinner begins with a plate of fresh vegetables: baby carrots that were picked that morning, washed radishes with their tops still on, sliced green pepper, and half a dozen thin rounds of cucumber.

all subjects and their verbs: *dinner/begins, that (referring to carrots)/were picked*
all pronouns and their antecedents: *that/carrots, their/radishes*

ASSIGNMENT 16A   MAINTAINING AGREEMENT WITH COMPOUND SUBJECTS

Read the following sentences. Circle each subject and underline each verb. If subjects and verbs agree, write *C* on the lines. If they do not, write a corrected version.

EXAMPLE

Neither the (lawyer) nor her (clients) <u>shows</u> any worries about winning the case.
Neither the lawyer nor her clients show any worries about winning the case.

1. Neither the witnesses nor the police officers was able to identify the hit-and-run driver positively.

   _____

   _____

2. Neither the witnesses nor the police officer were able to identify the hit-and-run driver positively.

   _____

   _____

3. Neither the car nor its occupants were seriously harmed. _____

   _____

4. Either you or the other driver were responsible for the accident. _____

   _____

5. Either the insurance company or you is going to pay for repairs. _____

   _____

Below you are provided with compound subjects and base-form verbs. Use these to write a sentence in the present tense, taking particular care that subjects and verbs agree.

EXAMPLE

   subject: *budding flowers and freshly cut lawns*   verb: *remind*
   Budding flowers and freshly cut lawns remind me of spring.

6. subject: *Barbara and Chris*   verb: *live* _____

   _____

7. subject: *papers and midterms*   verb: *challenge* _____

   _____

8. subject: *each paper and midterm*   verb: *become* _____

   _____

9. subject: *my sister and confidante*   verb: *visit* _____

   _____

ASSIGNMENT 16B   MAINTAINING VERB AGREEMENT WITH COLLECTIVE-NOUN OR INDEFINITE-PRONOUN SUBJECTS

In each sentence below, circle the subject and underline the main verb. Indicate whether the subject is a collective noun or an indefinite pronoun. If the subject and verb agree, write *C* on the lines that follow; if the subject and verb do not agree, rewrite the sentence so that the verb agrees with its subject.

EXAMPLE

(None) of the employees is able to substitute for you on Friday.
Subject is an indefinite pronoun.
None of the employees are able to substitute for you on Friday.

1. The group that white-water canoes the Nahanni River go home deeply affected by the experi-
    ence. *Subject is* _____

    _____

2. Neither of these auditioners are right for the part.

    Subject is _____

    _____

3. Most of those who commute use the same form of transportation every day.

    Subject is _____

    _____

4. That band play a spirited rendition of "God Save the Queen."

    Subject is _____

    _____

5. Some of this painting is absolutely brilliant. *Subject is* _____

    _____

ASSIGNMENT 16C REVIEWING SUBJECT-VERB AGREEMENT

Read each sentence below. If all subjects and verbs agree, write *C* on the lines. If there are errors of
agreement, rewrite the sentence on the lines provided.

1. The hands of the clock says 3:15.

    _____

2. Given her recent experience, she now agrees that alcohol is a dangerous drug.

    _____

    _____

3. Whenever it rain, I wear a coat.

    _____

4. The trains arrive daily at 2:30 and at 5:00.

    _____

5. The telephone operator who told me the arrival times were unnecessarily rude.

   _____

   _____

6. Among the best dishes in that restaurant are grilled lamb.

   _____

   _____

7. One of their great hopes in the last several years have been a trip to Scotland.

   _____

   _____

8. The glaucous gull and the western gull is often found inland during the stormy winter months.

   _____

   _____

9. Rum and Coke combines to make a popular alcoholic drink.

   _____

10. Pie and ice cream have always been our favourite dessert.

   _____

11. Each Saturday and Sunday morning is dedicated to sleeping late.

   _____

12. Tom and Liz, who also happens to be married to each other, each wears glasses.

   _____

   _____

13. Neither a graphic artist nor three proofreaders has been able to improve this poster. _____

   _____

14. Either the camp leaders or the campers themselves are required to clean the mess hall after each

   meal. _____

   _____

15. The team is voting for team captain now.

   _____

16. The parliamentary committee differ on the question of privatizing the Crown corporation.

   _____

   _____

17. Good news often go unreported.

   _____

18. Anybody taller than six feet know it can be difficult to find clothes that fits.

_____

_____

19. It is mathematics that cause me the most trouble in university.

_____

20. The end of those last few university weeks arrives with a strange mixture of gladness and

sorrow. _____

_____

ASSIGNMENT 16D MAKING PRONOUNS AGREE WITH COMPOUND OR COLLECTIVE-NOUN ANTECEDENTS

Identify the pronouns and their antecedents in each of the sentences below. If the pronouns are used inaccurately, rewrite the sentence to correct the errors. If the sentence is correct, write _C_ on the lines provided.

EXAMPLES

Whenever Leigh and Jack go out, Shelly stays with their children.
Pronouns/antecedents: their/Leigh and Jack
<u>C</u>
The goat and the two sheep have cropped that pasture right down to their roots.
Pronouns/antecedents: their/pasture
<u>The goat and the two sheep have cropped that pasture right down to its roots.</u>

1. Deer and bobcat populations stabilized once its habitats were preserved.

Pronouns/antecedents: _____

_____

2. By August, each gardener and homeowner is proud of their crop of squash.

Pronouns/antecedents: _____

_____

3. Tonight either Luc or Marie will have to take the projector home in his car.

Pronouns/antecedents: _____

_____

4. Nobody saw him, but the Anderson brothers washed Mrs. Wright's car.

Pronouns/antecedents: _____

_____

5. Bravo Company has decided that it will take separate cars to camp and meet by the mess hall at

noon. _Pronouns/antecedents:_ _____

_____

6. The committee has unanimously agreed to forward its recommendations.

   Pronouns/antecedents: _____

   _____

7. Jenny or she called their parents with the good news.

   Pronouns/antecedents: _____

   _____

ASSIGNMENT 16E MAKING PRONOUNS AGREE WITH INDEFINITE PRONOUNS AND AVOIDING SEXIST USAGE

Some of the following sentences use pronouns that unnecessarily identify the gender of an antecedent and thereby seem to exclude one sex. Some sentences may also contain errors of agreement between pronouns and indefinite-pronoun antecedents. In either case, circle the incorrect or sexist pronoun and write the correct one above it. If you need to alter the antecedent, feel free to do so. If the sentence does not need revision, write a *C* next to it.

EXAMPLES

Doctors study

A doctor studies for years in order to provide the best care for his patients. [their]

their rounds

All golfers should be finished with his or her round by 5:30.

1. Some of those trees lose their leaves quite early in the fall.

2. Few of the postal workers finished his shift early that day.

3. A woman must consider her values and priorities before taking a new job, just as a man must consider his.

4. Go find a nurse and ask her for a pain pill.

5. More of our first-year students change his or her majors than did so five years ago.

6. Anybody who has finished the course should receive his certificate in two weeks.

7. In 1980, anyone in Quebec had to make their own decision about the future of their province.

— 17 —

Using Adjectives and Adverbs

EXERCISE 17.1 WRITING WITH ADJECTIVES AND ADVERBS

Use the following guidelines to help you write a paragraph, on your own paper, about a summer activity that you enjoy.

1. Identify three summertime activities you enjoy.
2. Think carefully about each of the activities you identified. Which of these three would be easiest to write about in just one paragraph?
3. What specific details about this activity will you need to include? Write phrases to answer this question, not sentences.
4. Now draft your paragraph, and lay the draft aside for a time.
5. Reread and revise your draft paragraph so that its descriptions are lively and accurate, making a special point to add more adjectives and adverbs in order to achieve this.
6. Now identify five adjectives and five adverbs from your paragraph. Copy the adjectives and adverbs on your paper below your paragraph. Indicate each word that each adjective or adverb modifies (for example, "*accurately*, an adverb modifying identify").

EXERCISE 17.2 USING *GOOD*, *WELL*, *BAD*, *BADLY*, *REAL*, AND *REALLY*

Underline the correct adjective or adverb in each of the following sentences.

EXAMPLE

A chef for over eight years, she cooks good/well.

1. Amanda and Henry look good/well in their tango outfits.
2. A strong introduction is real/really important in a technical report.
3. The climbers hope the weather will be good/well for tomorrow's ascent.
4. After a weekend of rest, Dan looked good/well again.
5. He painted that fence bad/badly.
6. Raising the sea chest proved real/really difficult for the divers.
7. The appraisers claimed that this desk is a real/really antique.
8. After sitting out all night on the counter, the pizza tasted bad/badly.

EXERCISE 17.3 USING COMPARATIVE AND SUPERLATIVE FORMS

The sentences that follow contain various kinds of comparisons. In each case, determine what is being compared and whether or not the correct form of adjective or adverb has been used. If the sentence is correct as written, write *C* in the space after the sentence. If the sentence is incorrect as written, put *I* in the space, underline the incorrect form, and write in the correct form.

EXAMPLE

thicker

Compared to Pizza Gallery's crust, the Downtowner's was <u>thickest</u>.   <u>I</u>

1. Three local pizza restaurants—Dumbo's, Pizza Gallery, and the Downtowner—compete for the larger share of the area's pizza business. _____

2. Of the three restaurants, only two, Dumbo's and Pizza Gallery, provide home delivery, with Dumbo's delivery time being the slowest. _____

3. Our tests show that a Dumbo's pizza took, on the average, six minutes longer to arrive than one from Pizza Gallery. _____

4. All three restaurants offered vegetarian pizzas, with the Downtowner having the fancier, most exciting version. _____

5. Overall, the biggest difference among these three restaurants was in atmosphere: the judges unanimously ruled that Dumbo's fantasyland theme made it the more enjoyable place to sit. _____

ASSIGNMENT 17A IDENTIFYING AND CORRECTING ADJECTIVE-ADVERB ERRORS

Read the paragraph below. There are several errors in the usage of adverbs and adjectives. Underline those errors, and write in the correct forms. The first error has been underlined and corrected for you.

clearly

That was our tennis summer. I remember so <u>clear</u> that the days were hot and the skies always looked cloudlessly. If the wind blew, it blew only occasional and rare. Two days after we opened a new can of balls, they'd bounce sluggish. Maybe on the first bounce they'd rise to our knees weary. Maybe they'd just lie there stupid like jellyfish. Or maybe it was we who felt tiredly. Even so, we played real good tennis. We played fierce and crazily in the three o'clock sun. That was the summer before the workforce claimed any of us, before any of us went happy to university, before any really goodbyes. That was our tennis summer.

ASSIGNMENT 17B USING COMPARATIVE AND SUPERLATIVE FORMS

In each case below, you are given an adjective or an adverb and a specified form. Write a sentence using the specified form correctly. Make sure that your sentences distinguish appropriately between adjectives and adverbs and that the terms of any comparisons are complete.

EXAMPLES

blue, superlative form
The sky this afternoon is the bluest that I've ever seen.

sleepy, comparative form
I'm sleepier today than I was yesterday.

1. *serious*, comparative form

   _____

   _____

2. *seriously*, superlative form

   _____

   _____

3. *confusing*, comparative form

   _____

   _____

4. *bad*, superlative form

   _____

   _____

5. *well*, superlative form

   _____

   _____

6. *ill*, comparative form

   _____

   _____

7. *many*, superlative form

   _____

   _____

8. *hungry*, comparative form

   _____

   _____

9. *difficult*, comparative form

   _____

   _____

10. *rewarding*, superlative form

   _____

   _____

Making Sentence-Level Choices: Conventions

PART V   PREVIEW QUESTIONS

These questions are designed to help you, the student, decide what you need to study. (Answers are found at the back of the book.)

1. Are the pronouns in these sentences used correctly? Mark *yes* or *no*.

    a) My father asked Joe if he was needed at the store. _____
    b) During the concert, they made a lot of noise. _____
    c) In Shakespeare's *Macbeth*, he makes Macbeth's motivation clear. _____
    d) When Jack saw how much the repairs would cost, he vowed to junk the car. _____

2. Do these sentences contain any unnecessary or confusing shifts in person, number, tense, mood, subject, or voice? Mark *yes* or *no*.

    a) Everyone brought their favourite food to the class pot-luck banquet. _____
    b) Students should bring their identification cards to the library. _____
    c) To revise a paper, one should first read it yourself and then give it to someone else. _____
    d) We planned to go by bus, but then it was decided that the subway would be quicker. _____

3. Are these independent clauses correctly joined? Mark *yes* or *no*.

    a) The snow piled up, but we went to school anyway. _____
    b) Elizabeth did not like the music, she listened politely. _____
    c) My mother put the cake by an open window a bird landed on it. _____
    d) The door was closed; my brother came in anyway. _____

4. Do these examples contain sentence fragments? Mark *yes* or *no*.

   a) Some kinds of guitars sound better than others. _____

   b) I think we could get there in an hour. If we hurry. _____

5. Do these sentences use modifiers correctly? Mark *yes* or *no*.

   a) Created under conditions some might think impossible to survive, this anthology of Inuit poems is a testament to the human spirit. _____

   b) After calling the doctor, the pills started to work. _____

   c) We will, if nothing else comes up, call our mother today. _____

6. Do these sentences have garbled grammatical structures? Mark *yes* or *no*.

   a) This book claims that in such large cities as New York and San Francisco, AIDS should be everyone's concern. _____

   b) Two days after the torrential rain, the earth seemed to come alive like never before the plants were so green. _____

   c) John owns many records, and CD player. _____

   d) Bart wanted chocolate, but Eileen orders vanilla chocolate chip, and they were all out anyway. _____

— 18 —

Maintaining Clear Pronoun Reference

EXERCISE 18.1 IDENTIFYING AND REVISING CONFUSING PRONOUN USAGE

Many of the sentences that follow contain potentially confusing pronoun usage. Re-write those sentences to clear up any such confusions. If the sentence is clear as written, write *C* on the lines.

EXAMPLE

> Mary asked Cathy if she was responsible for the car accident.
> <u>Mary asked Cathy, "Am I responsible for the car accident?"</u>

1. During the student union election campaign, the Rahey-Utgoff debates forced him to articulate his positions.

   _____

   _____

2. The council, the mayor, and the city controller agree that her management style must change.

   _____

   _____

3. Jack liked Yvette and was still technically going steady with Sheila; finally, he decided to ask her to the prom.

   _____

   _____

4. The union representative called me last night at home and asked me if I was ready to go on strike today; I told him I still wasn't sure.

   _____

   _____

5. When Barbara and Donald first met with the marriage counsellor, she did not know how the session would go.

   _____

   _____

EXERCISE 18.2 USING *WHO, WHICH, THAT, YOU,* AND *THEY*

Read the following sentences, paying particular attention to pronoun usage. If the sentences use pronouns in appropriate and clear ways, write *C* on the lines. If pronouns are used in vague or inappropriate ways, revise the sentence.

EXAMPLES

> Most college classes require homework. They complain about it, but they do it.
> Most college classes require homework. Students complain about it, but they do it.

> The pilot whale who beached itself yesterday swam back out to sea this morning.
> The pilot whale that beached itself yesterday swam back out to sea this morning.

1. We had planned on watching *Masterpiece Theater* on Sunday evening, but since they were having transmission problems, we watched the CBC movie instead.

2. Parents should remember their own childhoods when setting standards for their children.

3. Customers which shop carefully for a used car can often make a satisfactory deal.

4. The Wrights expected a large crowd on Halloween night, and sure enough, they came to their door one after another.

5. Typing classes bore you when you're taking them, but afterward, you're glad you can type.

6. A dog who has been specially trained can give a blind person new mobility.

7. Whenever you walk into that stereo store, they come right up to you rather than letting you browse.

ASSIGNMENT 18A IDENTIFYING AND REVISING VAGUE, AMBIGUOUS, OR WORDY PRONOUN USAGE

Read the following portion of a letter written by a first-year university student to a school board member. The letter has been altered to include several kinds of pronoun errors. Underline all problematic pronouns. Then, on your own paper, rewrite the letter to eliminate problems of pronoun usage.

I am a former student of Hillsboro High School that is now attending the University of British Columbia as a first-year student in engineering physics. Several friends which graduated in my class are also attending U.B.C. and are having a hard time with their classes. To graduate from high school, they took the bare minimum requirements, and they are not enough to prepare them for university. After all, most university classes build on what you have already learned. And if they don't already know the foundations, it is going to be hard to pass the class. One example is Chemistry 204. It is a class that starts off with the basics, but after two weeks, they are 200 pages into the book. Without a good high school chemistry class as background, they're lost. It is important that each school board member consider his duty to students and look into this lack of preparation. Action is needed to improve new students' chances for success in university.

Apply the directions given at the top of this assignment to the passage reprinted below.

Once Darlene and Chris got the computer components out of boxes and onto the living room floor, then the real fun began. The instructions said on page A-2 that the short cable was supposed to plug into the C.P.U. in the back, with the other end plugging into the monitor. Unfortunately, they had no idea what a "monitor" was. To them, reading them was like reading Greek. After an hour of anger and frustration, they decided to forget it, and stacked them in the corner. Eventually, they paid a friend a free dinner to set up the system.

ASSIGNMENT 18B MAINTAINING CLEAR PRONOUN REFERENCE

Read the sentences below. If they use pronouns in clear, concise, and unambiguous ways, write *C* on the lines. Revise any sentences that use pronouns in wordy, vague, or ambiguous ways. Make sure your revision is concise, clear, and unambiguous.

EXAMPLE

When Barry discussed wages with Ted, he understood he would get a raise.

ACCEPTABLE REVISIONS

When Barry discussed wages with Ted, Barry understood Ted would get a raise.
When Barry discussed wages with Ted, Ted promised him a raise.

1. That year, when the delegates voted, they endorsed Wayne Morse. _____

_____

2. The picture hanging on the wall that you drew has provoked many favourable comments. _____

_____

3. The picture hanging on the wall that you drew has provoked many favourable comments, even

though it is peeling in places. _____

_____

_____

4. She plans to drive her Rover over Santiam Pass, which has given her trouble in the past. _____

_____

43

5. The plumbing company placed an order with Lee Tool & Die, but it was sold before they could fill it. _____

_____

6. We painted over the graffiti on the fence that offended us and bordered our parking lot. _____

_____

7. The committee discussed one proposal to raise taxes and another proposal to freeze them; eventually they passed it. _____

_____

_____

8. The landscape design program that you are interested in has four openings next year; that makes it a competitive program! _____

_____

_____

9. Negotiators reached a settlement after fifteen weeks that included two holidays and new provisions for vacation time. _____

_____

_____

10. It was said by witnesses that the car barrelled around the corner that hit me and swerved to my left. _____

_____

Recognizing Shifts

EXERCISE 19.1 IDENTIFYING AND REVISING CONFUSING SHIFTS IN TENSE

Read the five sentences that follow. Underline the verbs. If the sentence is correct as written, write *C* on the lines. If the sentence needs revising to eliminate confusing tense shifts, rewrite the sentence on the lines.

EXAMPLE

The barn swallows <u>return</u> about the same time that school <u>recessed</u> for spring break.
The barn swallows return about the same time that school recesses for spring break.

1. Ann measures the flour and poured it into the bowl. _____

_____

2. We paint the inside wall Friday, work in the garden on Saturday, and went to the beach on

Sunday. _____

_____

3. Jack swims like a fish and eats like a pig. _____

_____

4. The winds, which were blowing at almost gale force, capsize the rubber raft just as it reached the

mouth of the river. _____

_____

_____

5. Sleeping late on Saturday morning is an indulgence that we've earned after working hard all

week. _____

_____

Read the following paragraph. Underline all the verbs. Then revise the paragraph so that the verb tenses are consistent and sensible. Pencil in your changes above the offending verbs.

The accident, which occurs on Bellfountain Road at approximately 11:30 Saturday night, left four people injured and resulted in the death of one cow belonging to Angus Groenur. According to Mr. Groenur, the cow will wander out onto the road through a vandalized part of his pasture fence and settled onto the warm pavement for the night. Said Mr. Groenur, "The pavement holds the day's heat, you know. They like to lie there if they can. It's like a big hot water bottle to them." Police said tire marks indicate that the Subaru was

swerving in an attempt to miss the cow.

EXERCISE 19.2   IDENTIFYING AND REVISING CONFUSING SHIFTS IN PERSON AND NUMBER

Many of the following sentences contain unnecessary shifts in person and number. Rewrite these sentences to eliminate those unnecessary (and potentially confusing) shifts. If a sentence is accurate as written, write *C* on the lines.

EXAMPLE

Zoo patrons should be sure to visit the aviary, and you shouldn't miss the elephant house, either.
Zoo patrons should be sure to visit the aviary, and they shouldn't miss the elephant house, either.

1. If one visits the local art museum, you will find on display paintings by Mary Pratt.

2. Sea anemones thrive in coastal tidepools, but it cannot survive outside the water for very long.

3. When amateur photographers take pictures, he or she often enjoys the activity as much as the finished prints.

4. Lewis and Clark both kept journals, even though they wrote under less than ideal conditions.

5. A weekend runner is a prime candidate for running-related injuries, especially if they get no exercise during the week.

6. Tourists should be aware that road crews are busy on Highway 34, and a driver should expect some delay at the Oglesby Bridge construction site.

7. Whenever newspaper carriers go on vacation, you should make sure that you have arranged for a substitute to take over your route in your absence.

_____

_____

_____

EXERCISE 19.3   AVOIDING SHIFTS BETWEEN DIRECT AND INDIRECT DISCOURSE

Find four printed sentences (or short groups of sentences) that you find interesting. Use these four sentences to write four of your own. In two of your sentences, directly quote your sources (direct discourse). In the other two, use paraphrase (indirect discourse). Make sure that you do not use both quotation and paraphrase in the same sentence. Use your own paper for this exercise. Follow the format of the examples.

EXAMPLES

Source sentence: "To me she is alive and to me she speaks."
Origin: West with the Night by Beryl Markham.
Discussion using direct discourse: In her wonderful book *West with the Night*, the aviator Beryl Markham writes of her plane, "To me she is alive and to me she speaks."

Source sentence: "Want everything, Hugh — but wish for nothing."
Origin: Famous Last Words by Timothy Findley
Discussion using indirect discourse: Before Mr. Mauberley leaps to his death, the advice he gives his son is to want everything in life, but to wish for nothing.

EXERCISE 19.4   AVOIDING SHIFTS IN TONE AND DICTION

Read the following paragraph carefully. You will find that most of it employs a reasonably formal, informative tone and level of diction. Underline any sentences or phrases that strike you as inappropriate in tone or diction. Then, on your own paper, rewrite the paragraph so that its tone is consistently appropriate.

Anyone interested in writing for publication should be aware of the existence of "vanity presses." Listen folks, these guys and gals are out to empty your wallet! Such companies are incorporated for the sole purpose of printing books *at the expense of their authors*. Such "publishers" do not provide any advance money against future royalties. In fact, vanity press publishers make no bones about the fact that they make no monetary investment in any book. Rather, the author (that's you, bucko!) provides the moola up front. You either send the cheque or they sit on your manuscript. Even advance payment from an author is no guarantee that a printed book will receive the kind of attention authors seek. The fact is, many bookstores assume that these books are turkeys and won't stock them. Many authors who've paid for vanity press publication end up with hundreds of books in their garages or basements. Such authors often feel both cheated and degraded.

EXERCISE 19.5   RECOGNIZING AND REVISING INAPPROPRIATE, UNNECESSARY, OR CONFUSING SHIFTS

The following passage contains several unnecessary shifts of the kind discussed in Chapter 19. Read the passage carefully, and underline any shifts you believe unnecessary or confusing. Then, on your own paper, rewrite the passage to eliminate these shifts.

Employees ought to follow these company guidelines whenever dealing with customers:

First, if you can't understand what some bozo is saying, you shouldn't say, "Huh?" Say instead, "Pardon me" or "I'm sorry." If one is receiving a phone order, say, "We seem to have a bad connection; could you repeat that please?"

Second, if one believes a customer's choice of apparel is inappropriate, one should not register disapproval. You ain't there to raise folks' fashion consciousness; you're there to provide courteous service.

Third, if you are sick and could not come to work that day, he or she should have called the store manager. One employee went home early before they told anyone. That was wrong too. Such absences result in customers who feel neglected and other employees who felt frustrated because of your absence on the sales floor.

Fourth, if you were obligated by store policy to say no to some big spender, follow your no with a yes. For example, if you say that a credit purchase has not been approved, make sure you said that the store welcomed personal cheques, or say, "We will gladly set this merchandise aside for you."

Following these four guidelines will help ensure that customers returned to our stores. And repeat customers (and solid sales figures) made for a stable and remunerative employer-employee relationship.

ASSIGNMENT 19A IDENTIFYING AND REVISING CONFUSING OR UNNECESSARY SHIFTS IN MOOD AND VOICE

Read the following sentences. Underline the verbs, and pay particular attention to any shifts in mood or voice. If those shifts appear unnecessary or confusing, rewrite the sentence. If a sentence is clear and well written in its original form, write *C* on the lines. If a sentence unnecessarily employs both the active and the passive voice, convert the passive verbs to active.

EXAMPLES

Ms. MacNaught read the plans carefully, and they were approved by her. [*unnecessary shift from active to passive*]
Ms. MacNaught read the plans carefully, and she approved them.

The dinner was prepared and was delivered by Fast Catering Co. [*no shift here*]
C

On race day, drive slowly and you should be careful of the competitors. [*unnecessary shift from imperative to indicative*]
On race day, drive slowly and be careful of the competitors.

1. The chair asked that Milena report the subcommittee's findings and presents its recommendations.

_____

_____

2. The roses were gathered by Lionel, and then he arranged them.

_____

3. The graduate school requires that a master's student pass exams and defends his or her thesis.

_____

_____

4. Before you leave tonight, water the plants and you should lock the doors.

_____

5. The construction company delivered lumber Monday afternoon, and the wiring and plumbing materials were delivered by them later in the week.

_____

_____

6. Say no to their request, but you should say it tactfully.

_____

7. Holiday traffic congested the parkway and delayed the wedding party's arrival by over an hour.

_____

_____

8. The credit company asks that an applicant fill out an application and returns it within fourteen days.

_____

_____

9. The invitation suggests that Tanya brings ice skates and arrive at two o'clock.

_____

_____

10. If Suzanne were to become president and if Kelly was elected treasurer, we would celebrate with a dinner out.

_____

_____

Identifying Comma Splices and Fused Sentences

EXERCISE 20.1 IDENTIFYING AND REVISING COMMA SPLICES AND FUSED SENTENCES BY SEPARATING INDEPENDENT CLAUSES OR BY LINKING THEM WITH A SEMICOLON

Read the sentences that follow. Identify comma splices with *CS*, fused sentences with *F*, and correct sentences with *C*. Revise the comma splices and fused sentences either by making the independent clauses separate sentences or by using a semicolon to link them. You should be able to explain your choice. Pencil in your revisions in the spaces above the sentences.

EXAMPLE

___F___ An unusual thunderstorm dumped over two centimetres of rain in less than an hour several area roads were flooded when drains were unable to carry the water away.

_____ 1. Georgia O'Keeffe's stunning use of colour helped make her one of America's great painters forsaking the art world of large cities, she lived much of her life painting landscapes in desert New Mexico.

_____ 2. Fashion designing demands a rigorous knowledge of fabric, of the human form, and of changing taste, it also demands daring, intuition, and an eagerness to set fashion rather than follow it.

_____ 3. Usually, we do not question the time slots that television programmers give to their shows we seem perfectly willing to absorb the routine tragedies of the evening news while we eat lasagna or macaroni and cheese.

_____ 4. Burglary and car theft continue to be a major problem in many larger cities and towns, added prison space, unfortunately, does not deal with the unemployment, drug addiction, or lack of education that experts often cite as causes of such crime.

_____ 5. A short-wave radio can bring listeners programs in a variety of languages broadcast from locations as widely separate as South Africa, Britain, Germany, Latin America, and Japan.

EXERCISE 20.2 LINKING INDEPENDENT CLAUSES WITH COMMAS AND CO-ORDINATING CONJUNCTIONS

In each of the cases that follow, two sentences are provided. Join the two sentences using a comma and an appropriate co-ordinating conjunction. Write these directly above the place where they should go. Reread each resulting compound sentence to make sure it sounds right to you.

EXAMPLE

,and

No biography of Shakespeare was written during his lifetime. Scholars continue to puzzle over his identity.

1. The crocuses and daffodils bloomed early. April turned out to be unseasonably warm.

2. Jack's employee evaluation was mostly positive. He was laid off due to a shortage of orders.

3. Claire was reading Ray Smith's *Lord Nelson Tavern*. She thought it a very strange book.

4. Maybe we should plan on discussing this tomorrow at the staff meeting. Maybe we should call a special meeting that would include the other working group.

5. Alice was concerned that her chemistry books were overdue. The due date stamped in the back told her she still had two days to return them.

EXERCISE 20.3 LINKING INDEPENDENT CLAUSES WITH SEMICOLONS AND CONJUNCTIVE ADVERBS OR TRANSITIONAL PHRASES

In each of the following cases, two sentences are provided. Join the two sentences using a semicolon and an appropriate conjunctive adverb or transitional phrase. Write these directly above the place where they should go. Reread each resulting sentence to make sure it sounds right to you.

EXAMPLE

Students returning to school after years at home or in the work force are often nervous about the transition.

;nonetheless

With good academic counselling and with good support at home, most succeed.

1. The sign urged that those of you who partake of alcoholic beverages refrain from the operation of your automobiles. If you drink, don't drive.

2. No rains fell in Saskatchewan for over six weeks. Grain farmers suffered significant losses.

3. With all the travelling we do, we couldn't possibly own a dog. The apartment rules forbid pets.

4. One month she can't talk or even sit up by herself. She's standing wobbly-legged against the furniture and calling, "Ma, Ma."

5. The hostile reviews of his novel *Jude the Obscure* caused Thomas Hardy considerable pain and distress. The criticism contributed to his decision to give up writing fiction.

ASSIGNMENT 20A REVISING COMMA SPLICES AND FUSED SENTENCES

Read the following passage, and underline all comma splices and fused sentences. Then, on your own paper, rewrite the passage. You may choose to continue to link independent clauses, or you may choose to punctuate them as separate sentences. You may add co-ordinating conjunctions, conjunctive adverbs, or transitional phrases as you wish. You may revise using dependent clauses or by converting two independent clauses into one. Make sure that your revised paragraph is grammatically correct and punctuated accurately. For each comma splice or fused sentence you rewrite, be ready to explain the reason for the particular revision you choose.

Perhaps the most striking fact about people is that they make things. When early October arrives, swallows migrate dogs get heavier coats snakes go into a kind of hibernation people knit themselves caps. People without caps and people with too many caps get together and invent the set of promises we call money. Having invented money, people pay other people to make parkas and slickers or they use money to buy kits and make these things themselves. Rain pelts down deer seek the densest cover they can find people build houses with roofs. When cats get cold, they curl into tight little balls. People invent insulation or they pay sheep ranchers to provide the wool that's made into warm shirts. When caribou get hungry, they have no choice but to seek a new range. When people get hungry, they don't move eventually they invent pizza. They figure out how to cure olives they figure out how to make thick bread crusts, they experiment with anchovies and pineapple they invent beer. Indeed, people are makers.

ASSIGNMENT 20B DISTINGUISHING BETWEEN CO-ORDINATING CONJUNCTIONS AND CONJUNCTIVE ADVERBS OR TRANSITIONAL PHRASES

Each question below presents you with a pair of sentences. Combine them as indicated using either a comma and a co-ordinating conjunction or a semicolon, a conjunctive adverb (or transitional phrase), and a comma.

EXAMPLE

The Russian processing ship remained stationary on the horizon. Several Russian trawlers fished for hake. (Combine using an appropriate conjunctive adverb.)
The Russian processing ship remained stationary on the horizon; meanwhile, several Russian trawlers fished for hake.

1. The birds were singing. The sunlight shone through the slats of the bedroom's Venetian blinds. (Combine using an appropriate co-ordinating conjunction.)

_____

_____

2. She awoke feeling unusually optimistic. She felt like she might sing out loud. (Combine using an appropriate transitional phrase.)

_____

_____

3. My diet plan says I can eat four ounces of fish for dinner. I could choose the same amount of chicken. (Combine using an appropriate co-ordinating conjunction.)

_____

_____

4. Deer are curious animals. They will often run a short distance, stop, and look back. (Combine using an appropriate conjunctive adverb.)

_____

_____

5. The sun rises early on a June morning. The chorus of robins and bluebirds and sparrows starts even earlier. (Combine using an appropriate conjunctive adverb.)

_____

_____

6. For a long time, childhood had seemed distant, forgotten. That morning, standing at the window and hearing geese, she remembered a little girl held by her father, both of them looking up. (Combine using a co-ordinating conjunction, a conjunctive adverb, or a transitional phrase.)

_____

_____

_____

Read the following sentences, paying particular attention to how they combine independent clauses. If a sentence is correct as written, write _C_ on the lines. If a sentence is incorrect as written, rewrite it on the lines provided. Make sure your revision uses an appropriate co-ordinating conjunction, conjunctive adverb, or transitional phrase. Make sure your revision is also punctuated accurately.

EXAMPLE

He could hear traffic noise behind him he could see the white-capped Pacific in front of him.
He could hear traffic noise behind him; however, he could see the white-capped Pacific in front of him.

7. Salal grows in dense, green bushes; but, when it blooms, the dainty blossoms are no larger than your smallest fingernail.

_____

_____

8. The lumber industry provides jobs for many workers in British Columbia as well as for some other provinces, even so, some Canadian jobs are lost when the logs are exported.

_____

_____

_____

9. Rattan furniture is constructed when the materials are wet and pliable; yet those same materials prove both tough and durable once they have dried.

_____

_____

_____

10. The leading economic indicators all registered modest drops yesterday hence the stock market dropped in today's trading.

_____

_____

11. The Academy Awards telecast is often criticized as boring and too long, however it consistently garners high ratings.

_____

_____

ASSIGNMENT 20C REVISING COMMA SPLICES AND FUSED SENTENCES BY USING DEPENDENT CLAUSES OR BY MAKING TWO INDEPENDENT CLAUSES INTO ONE INDEPENDENT CLAUSE

Each case below features a comma splice or a fused sentence. Revise the incorrect sentence in two ways: (A) by making one of the independent clauses a dependent clause, and (B) by converting the two independent clauses to one independent clause.

EXAMPLE

Twentieth-century studies courses carry three credits they fulfil the requirements for electives in humanities.

A. REVISION USING A DEPENDENT AND AN INDEPENDENT CLAUSE

Twentieth-century studies courses, which carry three credits, fulfil the requirements for electives in humanities.

B. REVISION USING A SINGLE INDEPENDENT CLAUSE

With three credits, twentieth-century studies courses fulfil the requirements for electives in humanities.

1. The School of Education receives applications from more individuals than it can admit the school carefully screens all applications.

   A. _____

   _____

   _____

   B. _____

   _____

   _____

2. The committee discussed the zoning variance for thirty minutes, the variance was then approved on a 5–3 vote.

   A. _____

   _____

   B. _____

   _____

3. The premier is a Liberal he has decided not to attend the national party convention this month.

   A. _____

   _____

B. _____

_____

4. Computer technology changes rapidly however few businesses can afford to take advantage of every new advance.

A. _____

_____

B. _____

_____

5. Breakfast consisted of fresh strawberries, homemade biscuits, and scrambled eggs, it was served promptly at 9 A.M.

A. _____

_____

B. _____

_____

— 21 —

Recognizing Sentence Fragments

EXERCISE 21.1 IDENTIFYING AND REVISING PHRASE FRAGMENTS

Several of the short passages that follow contain phrase fragments. Read each passage sentence by sentence. Underline the fragments. Then revise the passage so that it contains only complete sentences. If the passage is correct as printed, write *C* beside the number of that passage. Use your own paper for this exercise.

EXAMPLE

The rhododendrons bloomed like orchids. Outside her window. As she typed, she could see them. Some of the blooms. Were a deep vermilion. Others were the pale, off-white colour. Of piano keys.

REVISION

The rhododendrons bloomed like orchids outside her window. As she typed, she could see them. Some of the blooms were a deep vermilion. Others were the pale, off-white colour of piano keys.

1. He was surprised at how the countryside changed. In just a few miles. The car dealerships and fast-food restaurants were replaced by rolling pasture. Enclosed by electrified fences.
2. When a woman is considering abortion, she ought to seek counselling. From family members, from her clergy, and from qualified social workers. She ought to talk candidly and at length. With the father. Certainly an interested party. Above all, she ought to listen. To her own conscience, then make her own decision.
3. Dancing in the rain was something Gene Kelly did in a movie. Called *Singing in the Rain*. It probably wasn't actually raining. During the filming. More likely, the movie crew rigged a rain machine over the set.
4. Designing advertising posters and brochures is great experience. It's particularly useful for journalism majors. Journalism 406 provides just such experience.
5. The committee has spent the last several days carefully reviewing your proposal. To extend the deadline for completion of your degree requirements. We are happy to be able to tell you that an extension has been granted. Your requirements must now be completed. By August of this year.

EXERCISE 21.2 IDENTIFYING AND REVISING COMPOUND-PREDICATE FRAGMENTS AND DEPENDENT-CLAUSE FRAGMENTS

Read the following brief paragraphs, and underline any sentence fragments. Then revise the paragraphs to eliminate the fragments. Write your revision on a separate page.

Community residents will have their final say tonight. When the city council convenes a special hearing on the proposed Sylvan Green Development Project. The project has already received preliminary approval from the council. The development proposal calls for the construction of two anchor stores in its first phase. And specifies widening McKean Boulevard to accommodate increased traffic. The developers, who have already invested over $300,000 in architectural fees and permits. Argue that all city zoning requirements have been met. Local residents and developers have clashed at two earlier meetings.

According to opposition leaders, residents worry. That nightly deliveries might cause considerable noise. And those opposed have also voiced concern over increased traffic at the school crosswalk at Oak and Fifty-sixth. When the hearing convenes tonight at 7:30 in council chambers. Those opposed to the development promise fireworks.

EXERCISE 21.3 IDENTIFYING AND REVISING SENTENCE FRAGMENTS

Read the following passage on test taking. You will notice several sentence fragments. Underline every fragment you find. Then, on your own paper, revise the passage. You may combine or rearrange sentences in any way you see fit, so long as you retain the original content. You need not eliminate every single fragment; if you decide to keep a fragment, copy it after your revision. Then briefly explain that decision.

How people take tests says something. About them as people. Some individuals worry. And do nothing but worry. They don't reread, they don't review their notes, and they don't discuss major issues with classmates. After all this, they may still be surprised. When the test day arrives and they aren't prepared. Other people worry, but they put that worry to work. These individuals use their worry. As motivation to make study plans. In addition to reviewing notes and doing some selective rereading. These students might also try to anticipate test questions. And then construct appropriate answers. In effect, they take practice tests. Then there are the people who don't worry at all. They don't take tests seriously. And probably don't spend much time in preparation. The most naturally gifted in this group. May still do reasonably well on tests. However, even the most naturally gifted may be cheating themselves. If they don't study. As my grandma used to say, "If you've never worked hard, how do you know how hard you can work?"

— 22 —

Recognizing Misplaced, Disruptive, and Dangling Modifiers

EXERCISE 22.1 IDENTIFYING AND REVISING MISPLACED MODIFIERS

Each of the following sentences contains a misplaced modifier. Underline it, and use an arrow to indicate its proper placement in the sentence.

EXAMPLE

Only Just Woollens sells yarn and related knitting supplies.

1. Barking, the chain link fence restrained the dog.
2. The computer system almost cost $2,000, but Michelle paid it in monthly instalments.
3. The sign said this: "Only at St. Anthony's, services are held on Sundays at 9:15 A.M."
4. Even the weather surprised the meteorologist.
5. Campers may play various games if it rains indoors.
6. The directions said to shut *on* the light inadvertently when we left the room.
7. Most days are warm enough nearly for swimming before lunch.

EXERCISE 22.2 IDENTIFYING AND REVISING SQUINTING MODIFIERS

Read each of the following sentences carefully. Underline any squinting modifiers you find. Then circle the two words or groups of words the writer might have wanted the squinting modifier to modify. If the sentence is clear as written, write *C* in the margin next to it.

EXAMPLE

(Rita thought) after the meeting (she would like to go home.)

1. Employees entering this area routinely are required to wear safety gear.

2. The defendant promised during the trial he would obey the judge's instructions.

3. Margie felt often Gerard was considerate and good with the children.

4. The tenants promised faithfully to honour the conditions of the lease.

5. People frequently argue about the role of Canadian forces overseas.

On a separate sheet of paper, rewrite each sentence with a squinting modifier twice: once to make the modifier modify only the first section of the sentence that you have circled, and a second time to make it modify only the second part that you have circled. After each pair of rewritten sentences, write a brief explanation of how they differ in meaning.

EXAMPLES

> After the meeting, Rita thought she would like to go home. [*The meeting was already over when Rita thought about going home.*]
> Rita thought she would like to go home after the meeting. [*Rita is thinking beforehand that she will want to go home when the meeting has finished.*]

EXERCISE 22.3   IDENTIFYING AND REVISING DANGLING MODIFIERS

Read the following passage, paying particular attention to phrase and clause modifiers. (The sentences are numbered for easy reference.) Underline any dangling phrases or clauses. Make a list of all the modifiers you have underlined and explain briefly why they are inaccurately used. Then rewrite the passage to clarify its content. Use your own paper for this exercise.

When stricken by spring fever, the results may be disastrous.[1] Although not fatal, this disease can lead to loss of productivity.[2] Consulting authorities, the specific symptoms include lassitude, a lack of motivation, an eagerness to spend long hours prone under sunlight, and an unwillingness to concentrate.[3] Enduring hard winters, spring fever is a particular problem.[4] Once May arrives, Torontonians have been known to leave their offices as early as 1 P.M. on Friday afternoons.[5] Happy at the return of good weather and hoping for good luck, "Gone Fishing" signs appear in Maritime shop windows.[6] Dotting the skies over Calgary, people admire hot-air balloons.[7] Actually, spring fever means trouble only to the manufacturers of small wading pools for children.[8] Though pleased by the avalanche of orders, factory buildings hum night and day to meet the demand.[9]

ASSIGNMENT 22A   IDENTIFYING AND REVISING DISRUPTIVE AND DANGLING MODIFIERS

Underline any dangling or disruptive modifiers (phrases or clauses) you find in each of the sentences below. Then revise the sentence so that it reads smoothly and clearly. If the sentence is fine as written, write *C* on the line.

EXAMPLES

> She sang in her first public concert a selection of traditional folk songs and ballads.
> In her first public concert, she sang a selection of traditional folk songs and ballads.

> Winded and tired, the race seemed endless.
> Winded and tired, he felt the race would never end.

1. Fresh fish, although more expensive and sometimes hard to locate, tastes better than fish that has been frozen. _____

   _____

2. After years playing chess the game got boring. _____

   _____

3. Dierdre decided to after a particularly bad week both at work and at home visit her sister for the weekend. _____

   _____

4. Looking both ways, the traffic was too heavy to cross the street safely. _____
_____

5. Eating his lunch, his stomach began to growl. _____
_____

6. John Davidson in *The Music Man*, which opened last night, got rave reviews. _____
_____
_____

7. Now that she is eleven and believes her parents know virtually nothing, Melissa has decided that
the telephone is her best friend. _____
_____
_____

8. Happy and no longer tired, the finish line appeared at last at the bottom of the hill. _____
_____
_____

9. Before jogging regularly, a good pair of running shoes should be purchased. _____
_____
_____

10. The candidate gave following a dinner of roast beef, peas, and mashed potatoes a speech
supporting the Prime Minister's foreign policies. _____
_____
_____

— 23 —

Maintaining Consistent and Complete Grammatical Structures

EXERCISE 23.1 MATCHING SUBJECTS AND PREDICATES

Read the following passage. Underline any sentences with faulty or unnecessarily wordy predication. Work on revising the passage to make it clearer. Add or clarify content if you feel that will make for a clearer final version. Use your own paper for this exercise. Sentences are numbered for easy reference.

The reason people can recognize a smooth collie is because they look like collies but when they're full grown their hair is short.[1] Smooth collies are where they have the same general build as their hairier cousins (called rough collies) and the same long noses.[2] But probably their most important characteristic is where like other collies they have great dispositions.[3] The nature of collies will accept abuse that would snarl or even bite.[4] Small children can sit on collies or hold their paws as if shaking hands.[5] Collies will even tolerate someone playing with their food.[6] Actually, collies are so lovable to hurt or tease them.[7] They're loyal, and they're so excited to see you in the morning that their brown eyes make you glad you got out of bed.[8] Collies are also superior intelligence.[9]

EXERCISE 23.2 USING ELLIPTICAL STRUCTURES CAREFULLY

Read the following sentences. If a sentence omits words that should be included or if it repeats words that could be omitted, revise the sentence on the lines provided.

EXAMPLES

Joey wanted to see a science fiction movie, Melanie wanted to see a romance movie, and Aaron stay home.
Joey wanted to see a science fiction movie, Melanie wanted to see a romance, and Aaron wanted to stay home.

Cathy arrived first, and Katie arrived ten minutes later.
Cathy arrived first, and Katie ten minutes later.

1. Kamal gets along well with Cecilia and Don but not Bev.

2. We could clearly hear Radio Moscow yesterday, but less today.

3. During the summer, Ben plays softball on Tuesdays, he plays tennis on Wednesdays, and he plays soccer on Thursdays.

61

4. Harold decided to take a nap, Michael decided to study for his chemistry test, and Susan to take a book back to the library.

_____

_____

_____

5. The car's exterior is blue, but the seats black vinyl.

_____

_____

ASSIGNMENT 23A   RECOGNIZING AND REVISING GARBLED PROSE

Read the following passage carefully. Look for omissions, incomplete comparisons, and any garbled or blurred pattern sentences, underlining any that you find. On your own paper, revise the passage to clarify its content. Sentences are numbered for easy reference.

Writers familiar with word processing programs have a variety of skills literally their fingertips.[1] Such writers can move paragraphs or sentences from one part of paper to another.[2] They can revise sentences or whole passages without that having to retype the entire document.[3] They can experiment with the sizes of the margins italic or boldface type.[4] Some printers are even equipped with adjustable pitch changes the number of characters can be printed on one line.[5] In short, word processing programs make revisions easy and no excuse for failing to revise.[6] For all of these reasons, writers who use computers are often considered more productive by employers.[7]

ASSIGNMENT 23B   IDENTIFYING AND REVISING CONFUSING SENTENCES

Read the following sentences aloud. If a sentence reads clearly and correctly, write a _C_ on the lines. If the sentence sounds confusing, revise the sentence and write your revision on the lines provided.

EXAMPLE

Allergies on an average spring day you will find many people suffering.
On an average spring day, you will find many people suffering from allergies.

1. The newspaper said that instead of beginning at 8:30, the sale would not open its doors until

9:30. _____

_____

2. On average, the rain here falls at a rate of 50% higher than east of the mountains.

_____

_____

3. Before we reorganized the books were stacked on those shelves reached as high as the ceiling.

_____

_____

4. I was stretched out on the grass, and the clouds looked like animals.

_____

5. Not only was the tape dispenser empty, and the light bulb had burned out.

_____

_____

6. Most electric coffeepots come equipped with a thermostat that shutting off the electricity when the pot boils dry. _____

_____

7. To find the financial aid office is on the third floor of the administration building.

_____

_____

ASSIGNMENT 23C CHECKING FOR INADVERTENT OMISSIONS AND FOR INCOMPLETE COMPARISONS

Read the sentences below, checking carefully for any omissions or faulty comparisons. If a sentence needs revising, write your new version on the lines provided. Add new content as necessary. If the sentence is accurate and acceptable as written, write *C* on the lines.

EXAMPLE

The small-screen colour television is more expensive.
The small-screen colour television is more expensive than the 19-inch black-and-white model.

1. Her play in today's match was better than yesterday. _____

_____

2. If we can believe the newspaper, the weather in Victoria yesterday was the same as St. John's.

_____

_____

3. The firewood was stacked neatly in wooden rack by the back door. _____

_____

_____

4. This piano is in better tune. _____

_____

5. Entitled *Dance on the Earth*, Margaret Laurence's memoir chronicles the life times of this admired Canadian author. _____

_____

_____

6. The Rambo movies appeal to a different audience than *Bambi*. _____

_____

_____

7. These days, summer boredom seems worse twelve-year-olds than it does for young children or

for teenagers. _____

_____

_____

8. Environment Canada claims that this is the warmest March on record. _____

_____

_____

9. On particular hot days, the railroad crossing gates descend and block traffic even though there is

no train in sight. _____

_____

_____

10. Although it is generally high in sodium and fat content, fast food tastes better. _____

_____

_____

Making Sentence-Level Choices: Style

PART VI PREVIEW QUESTIONS

These questions are designed to help you, the student, decide what you need to study. (Answers are found at the back of the book.)

1. Can the following sentences be revised to be more concise? Answer yes or no.

   a. Contemporary rock groups performing now frequently make use of synthesizers.

   _____

   b. The election did not resolve anything. _____

2. Underline the co-ordinating conjunctions in the following sentences.

   a. Siberian huskies have thick fur so they will never be cold in the winter. _____

   b. Usually Carolyn is never late but this time she missed her train. _____

3. Can a subordinate clause ever stand on its own? Answer yes or no. _____

4. Underline the subordinate clauses in the following sentences.

   a. When the rain started, Jocelyn and I took shelter in a book store.

   b. The man who gave me this watch seemed to be desperate.

   c. Carolyn was late even though she left an hour early.

5. Do the following sentences use parallel structures correctly? Answer yes or no.

   a. We will carry the fight for women's rights into the schools, the churches, and into the legislatures. _____

   b. It is better to remain silent and to have people take you for a fool than to speak and to remove all doubt. _____

c. Hard work, long nights in the library, and constantly revising your essays will guarantee you good grades. _____

6. Identify any of these stylistic weaknesses in the following sentences: passive verbs, wordiness, weak verbs. If none of these weaknesses are present, mark a *C* next to the sentence.

a. It is necessary that everyone arrive at the ticket booth at the same time. _____

b. Pianists often wrestle with the technically treacherous passages of Bach's *Goldberg Variations*. _____

c. Although the bronze and the silver medals were won by the other team, the gold was won by us. _____

d. Today the weather was bad. _____

e. My paper topic was approved by my history teacher. _____

— 24 —

Constructing Effective Sentences

EXERCISE 24.1   REVISING WORDY PROSE

Read the following passage, paying particular attention to any sentences that seem to you unnecessarily wordy. Work on a revision of the passage, and copy your best version onto a separate sheet of paper. By way of example, a revision of the first sentence follows the passage.

If I think back to growing up in the city, when I was a child, a mere youngster, I can see again in my mind's eye and remember the look of Toronto's street cars. Their parallel tracks or iron wheel guides crisscrossed downtown streets, boulevards, and byways (but not alleys), and their overhead wires mirrored the tracks. The cars I remember were big and sturdy, as were all street cars. They made a loud, rumbling noise that made the streets shake. The street cars I remember were also run down inside and decrepit, with paint red in colour and peeling and with seats oozing cotton stuffing or padding. Perhaps because the cars themselves were in sorry shape, it always seemed that the riders were in similar condition. Of the riders I remember from that point in time, a few continue to remain in memory: some of them were drunk, some just rambled to themselves, and some just needed showers. For a small child of perhaps four or five years in age, riding in a street car was an experience that produced an interesting mixture of fear and excitement. The fear was of those other passengers: Would they simply continue to remain dozing peacefully? Would they stand up raving? Would they hurt or do violence to children? The excitement came from experiencing something unfamiliar, something new, something unpredictable.

REVISED FIRST SENTENCE

If I think back to my childhood in the city, I can remember Toronto's street cars.

ASSIGNMENT 24A   USING CLIMACTIC ORDER

Revise the following sentences so that they use climactic order.

EXAMPLE

Skiing is expensive and time-consuming, but it is also a lot of fun, which I never knew because I had not tried it.

67

REVISION

Because I had never tried to ski, I was surprised to find that, although expensive and time-consuming, it is a lot of fun.

1. Coast Guard personnel conduct boating safety classes, must sometimes risk their own lives to save others, and routinely monitor emergency radio channels.

   _____

   _____

2. Lester B. Pearson became Prime Minister after serving as a member of the federal Cabinet and after a distinguished career as a diplomat.

   _____

   _____

3. Jamaica produces many crops, including sugarcane (its most important farm product), citrus fruits, bananas, and allspice.

   _____

   _____

4. Most agree that Martin Luther King's career as a civil rights leader reached its high point when he addressed over 200,000 protesters at the Washington Monument in August 1963; King helped to establish the Southern Christian Leadership Conference in 1957 and became its first president that same year.

   _____

   _____

   _____

   _____

   _____

   _____

ASSIGNMENT 24B BEING CONCISE

The sentences below are all either redundant or plagued by all-purpose modifiers. Rewrite each sentence so that it is concise. If you must supply content (instead of all-purpose modifiers), do so.

EXAMPLES

We definitely had an absolutely and quite literally great time at the beach.
The condominium salesperson repeated again that the unsold units were few in number and that we would receive a free gift for taking a tour of the grounds.

REVISIONS

The sunny weather and temperatures in the high twenties made for an enjoyable weekend at the beach.
The condominium salesperson told us that only a few unsold units remained, and he promised us a gift for taking a tour of the grounds.

1. At the present time, it is true and continues to remain the case that welfare reform is a really major, central, and important issue. _____

2. It is believed by many experts who have studied this problem that workers who labour on graveyard shifts exhibit a tendency to commit more errors than workers commit during the shift during the day. _____

3. Von requested of me and asked that in the event that he could not return to the campus by 9 A.M., at that point in time I ought to turn in his paper for him. _____

4. It is true that the sandwich that you made tasted really great. _____

5. The consensus of agreement that we have reached as a result of our discussions is that the paper originally scheduled on the calendar to be turned in on Monday will now be due on the following Friday thereafter. _____

Creating Co-ordinate and Subordinate Structures

EXERCISE 25.1 USING CO-ORDINATION AND SUBORDINATION FOR SPECIAL EFFECT

On a separate sheet of paper, compose two sentences using repeated co-ordination and two sentences using repeated subordination. Then find one published example of either repeated co-ordination or repeated subordination and copy out the sentence(s) using it. (College readers and anthologies of essays are good sources of examples, as are college handbooks and news magazines.)

ASSIGNMENT 25A USING CO-ORDINATION

Use co-ordination to combine each pair of simple sentences. Make sure the resulting sentence is properly punctuated. Do not use the same conjunction more than once.

EXAMPLE

> The geography test had me worried. I studied for two hours in the library.
> The geography test had me worried, so I studied in the library for two hours after lunch.

1. Sharon wanted higher grades on her written work. She studied to improve her spelling.

   _____

   _____

2. During the storm, we heard tree trunks snap. We saw the weird, blue light of electrical transformers as they shorted out.

   _____

   _____

3. The sun did not come out today. The rain never stopped.

   _____

   _____

4. Karen thought she would have trouble with the math class. She earned an A on the last test.

   _____

   _____

5. Saturday we will have spaghetti for dinner. We may have beef stroganoff.

   _____

   _____

ASSIGNMENT 25B USING SUBORDINATION

For each of the five cases below, combine the given simple sentences by making one of the sentences a dependent clause. (More than one correct answer is possible for each sentence.)

EXAMPLE

The woman sold me a sweater. She seemed to be about Debbie's size.
The woman who sold me this sweater seemed to be about Debbie's size.

1. You gave me a computer disk. The disk was the wrong size.

    _____

    _____

2. Students make decisions about careers. Students should think about what makes them happy as well as about what will make them wealthy.

    _____

    _____

    _____

3. Reggie was sick with a cold last week. He turned his paper in on time.

    _____

    _____

    _____

4. A dog bit their daughter. Emily and John were looking for a pet.

    _____

    _____

5. Greg's works were featured for three weeks at the Guistina Gallery. His works include both paintings and drawings.

    _____

    _____

    _____

— 26 —

Creating and Maintaining Parallel Structures

EXERCISE 26.1   USING PARALLEL STRUCTURES IN REVISION

Read the passage that follows, paying particular attention to any sentences that could use parallel structures but do not. Remember that sometimes combining sentences will yield useful parallel structures. Underline any sentences that you would want to revise to make their structures parallel. Revise the passage, and copy your best version on a separate page. The sentences are numbered for easy reference.

When faced with the task of moving from one town to another, we decided to save money by tackling the entire job ourselves.[1] We quickly discovered that moving was not fun—it was working hard.[2] The physical work was tiring enough, but we had more trouble with the decision making.[3] Should we sell Aunt Maude's needlepoint pillow with the moth hole, or should it be lovingly packed in a box?[4] Occasionally we agreed on such things, but more often our opinions did not coincide.[5] Then we either continued packing in a tense silence, or some joke would defuse the situation.[6]

Through trial and making mistakes, we discovered that the heaviest items should go into the smallest containers.[7] Thus, books went into the smallest boxes; mid-size boxes held small lamps (minus the shades), and shoes.[8] And the biggest boxes bulged with the lightest goods, such as clothing, bedding, or what came from the linen closet.[9] We also learned that not only must all boxes be carefully packed, stacking is important.[10] Small, heavy boxes crush those which are large and airy.[11] But neither careful packing nor an adequate job of stacking could tell us exactly what was inside an unlabelled box.[12]

EXERCISE 26.2   ANALYSING PARALLEL STRUCTURES AND THEIR EFFECTS

Below are two sample passages, each presented in three different versions. Some versions employ parallel structures; others do not. On your own paper, indicate whether each version uses parallel structures, and, in one or two sentences, describe how the effect of each version on the reader differs from the effects of the other two versions. Do not be concerned with which version is better but with the impressions or feelings each conveys.

1. a) To Rita, Ed was a real catch; to her parents, he was an aimless drifter.
    b) To Rita, Ed was a real catch. An aimless drifter is what he seemed like to her parents.
    c) Either Ed was a real catch, which is what Rita thought, or he was just an aimless drifter, which is what Rita's parents thought.
2. a) Joe wants a big house and a fast car. Joe wants nice landscaping and a built-in swimming pool. Joe wants a lot of things.
    b) Joe wants a big house, a fast car, nice landscaping, and a built-in swimming pool; Joe wants a lot of things.
    c) Joe wants a big house. You should see the car he wants to buy. Nice landscaping is important to him, too. After he has all of that, the next thing on his list of things to buy is a built-in swimming pool. An awful lot of things is what Joe wants.

ASSIGNMENT 26A **USING PARALLEL STRUCTURES**

Read the sentences below. If the sentence employs accurate parallel structures, underline these structures and write "structures parallel" on the lines provided. If the sentence does not employ accurate parallel structures, write an accurately parallel revision on the line. Do not worry if your revision changes the content of the original; the idea is to write sentences with accurately parallel structures.

EXAMPLES

Some kids love reading, and for others it's soccer that they love.
Some kids love reading, and others love soccer.

Take it or leave it.
structures parallel

1. Pierre preferred to do his own landscaping, his own roofing, and install the carpet himself.

   _____

2. This company not only designs and manufactures superior hardware, it also provides first-class customer service.

   _____

   _____

3. On a clear day, you can see west to the Bay of Fundy, Minasville in the east, and north to Parrsboro.

   _____

   _____

4. The firefighters asked for calm and that spectators remain a safe distance away.

   _____

   _____

5. This week, Parliament may vote on child care legislation, or after the upcoming holiday recess.

   _____

6. Comprehensive health insurance, making sure everyone kept their jobs, and the right to strike—those were the union's main demands.

   _____

   _____

   _____

7. The road wound down out of heavily forested mountains, through pastureland, and then you come to the city.

   _____

   _____

8. She ate cold pizza for breakfast, and lobster was what she ate at dinner. _____

_____

9. I'm not swayed by candidate A with his fiery rhetoric, nor by candidate B with his impossible promises.

_____

_____

10. Some of the bloodiest fighting of World War I occurred at the Somme River, just as lots of people landing on the beaches at Normandy were killed during World War II.

_____

_____

_____

— 27 —
Varying Sentence Structures

EXERCISE 27.1   IDENTIFYING VARIOUS SENTENCE OPENINGS

Two versions of a passage appear below. Read the first version, then the second. In the second version, underline any new or changed material, and number it as (1) a single-word transition, (2) a prepositional, verbal, or absolute phrase, or (3) a dependent clause. As an example, the first change has been underlined and identified for you.

The first afternoon and evening was sunny and hot. We ate dinner in a meadow overlooking the Pacific, and we watched the sun set. It was almost every shade of orange, red, and purple going down. We went to bed expecting good weather. It rained that night. We woke up in the morning and tried to make pancakes while staying warm in our sleeping bags. Some of the batter spilled onto the sleeping bags. The spill made an unpleasant mess.

(3)

Because that first afternoon and evening was sunny and hot, we ate dinner in a meadow overlooking the Pacific. As we ate, we watched the sun set. It was almost every shade of orange, red, and purple going down.

After such a brilliant sunset, we went to bed expecting good weather. Unfortunately, it rained that night.

Disappointed only a little bit, we woke up in the morning and tried to make pancakes while staying warm in our sleeping bags. Because we were clumsy and maybe still a little sleepy, some of the batter spilled onto the sleeping bags. As you can imagine, this made for an unpleasant mess.

EXERCISE 27.2   REVISING PROSE BY VARYING SENTENCE LENGTHS AND SENTENCE OPENINGS

Revise the following passage by varying sentence lengths and by varying sentence openings. You may combine or recombine sentences; you may add new content. Make sure that your final version is smoother than the original version. Copy your final version on a separate sheet of paper.

Land use issues are important. We don't often pay attention to them. We do pay attention when a developer decides to change the character of our neighbourhood. Our family knows about this because the field behind our house has been slated for clearing, grading, and construction. Our kids have played there for years. A new shopping centre will be built. That means cars, noise. It could mean new shops and a better local selection of goods. It might mean a fancy new restaurant or two. Sometimes, we think the development is a good idea. It will benefit the community and provide jobs. Sometimes, we don't want that field to change. The whole family goes to planning commission hearings. We listen to the developer. We listen to our neighbours. Land use isn't some foggy, distant issue anymore. It's as close as our backyard.

EXERCISE 27.3 ADDING SENTENCE VARIETY

Use your own paper to freewrite on the topic of why you, personally, are in school. What brought you to university? What is keeping you here? What are your goals? If these are somewhat confusing questions to you, talk about why they are confusing. Write quickly and freely, and do not censor yourself. Do not worry about spelling or grammar. Try to fill at least two-thirds of a page.

When you have finished, reread and revise your freewriting. Your goal is to produce at least two clear and coherent paragraphs using at least *five* of the seven sentence types identified as follows:

1. simple sentence
2. compound sentence
3. complex sentence
4. compound-complex sentence
5. periodic sentence
6. cumulative sentence
7. interrogative, imperative, or exclamatory sentence

Copy your final version onto another sheet of paper, placing the number corresponding to the appropriate type after each sentence. Every sentence in your final version should have a number after it.

ASSIGNMENT 27A WRITING SENTENCES OF VARYING LENGTHS

Revise each of the following sentences as specified. Be ready to discuss the differences of meaning and emphasis between the original and your revision.

EXAMPLES

Since we've lost two games already and since this week's opponent has lost only one game, you can see that it's really important that we come out on top. (Summarize in a short sentence.)
We need to win!

It was Sunday afternoon. The sun was shining. The hammock was in the backyard. It was a perfect day for resting in the hammock. (Combine into one long sentence.)
That sunny Sunday afternoon was perfect for resting in the hammock in the backyard.

1. You should stop playing or looking at the gravel or doing whatever you're doing out there in the street because a large dump truck is coming. (Summarize in a short sentence.)

   _____

   _____

2. First you strip off the original finish, then complete any rough sanding, then smooth all of the table's exposed surfaces with fine steel wool, and then apply the new finish. (Break into several short sentences.)

   _____

   _____

   _____

   _____

3. Some people have trouble with math. Often they say they study and study. Then they take the test. They are usually disappointed with the results. (Combine into one smooth sentence.)

_____

_____

_____

4. Persistence pays. (Write a longer single sentence version that emphasizes the importance of persistence.)

_____

_____

_____

5. The clam chowder is good. The clam chowder is thick. Clam chowder and French bread make a good meal. Sometimes, they go well with a glass of Riesling. The clam chowder is served on Fridays. It's served at lunchtime. (Combine into one or two smooth sentences.)

_____

_____

_____

_____

Creating Memorable Prose

ASSIGNMENT 28A REVISING BY CHOOSING STRONGER VERBS

Weak verbs and unnecessarily wordy constructions plague the following sentences. Revise the sentences by substituting stronger verbs.

EXAMPLES

It is necessary that the cast arrive for rehearsal at 6 P.M.
The cast must arrive for rehearsal at 6 P.M.

A large amount of electrical energy is a requirement for aluminum production.
Aluminum production requires a large amount of electrical energy.

1. The murder mystery on television was so boring that I fell asleep.

   _____

2. There were many parents in the parking lot waiting to pick up their children.

   _____

3. In many cities, burglars are a threat to neighbourhood security.

   _____

4. It is said by most political cartoonists that a candidate's looks are more important than a candidate's positions on the issues.

   _____

5. In Munich, there were excited Canadian fans who watched figure skater Kurt Browning capture his third consecutive world championship.

   _____

   _____

6. The personal lives of actors and actresses are of interest to many of their fans.

   _____

7. A requirement of many computer programs is at least 256 kilobytes of memory.

   _____

ASSIGNMENT 28B CHOOSING BETWEEN THE ACTIVE AND THE PASSIVE VOICE

Identify the following sentences as either active or passive. Then note the intended emphasis of each.

If the original version accomplishes that emphasis, write *OK*. If the original version does not accomplish that emphasis, rewrite the sentence by changing its voice.

EXAMPLES

My supervisor approved your memo.
Sentence is <u>active</u>. Intended emphasis: the memo
<u>The memo was approved by my supervisor.</u>

The weather forecast was given as the last news item.
Sentence is <u>passive</u>. Intended emphasis: the weekend news anchor
<u>The weekend news anchor gave the weather forecast as her last news item.</u>

Kenyan coffee is grown in Africa.
Sentence is <u>passive</u>. Intended emphasis: the coffee
<u>OK</u>

1. An honours medal was won by my sister Kate.

   Sentence is _____. Intended emphasis: my sister Kate

   _____

2. Dogs and cats are frequently disturbed by the explosions of July 1 fireworks.

   Sentence is _____. Intended emphasis: dogs and cats

   _____

3. You are hereby summoned to appear in Small Claims Court on July 21 at 10 A.M.

   Sentence is _____. Intended emphasis: the Province of Ontario

   _____

4. In summer, soaring red-tail hawks are often seen by us high over the meadows.

   Sentence is _____. Intended emphasis: we

   _____

5. In the next eight minutes, seismographers recorded five aftershocks.

   Sentence is _____. Intended emphasis: the aftershocks

   _____

ASSIGNMENT 28C COMPOSING SENTENCES THAT USE SPECIAL EFFECTS

Chapter 28 identifies three kinds of sentences using structures that create special effects. One kind uses repetition, the second uses antithesis, and the third uses inversion. For this exercise, compose a sentence of each kind. An example of each kind of sentence is given.

EXAMPLE OF REPETITION

Once I sweep out the garage, once I mow the lawn, once I wash and vacuum the car, once I pick up my sweater at the cleaner's, once I balance the cheque book and pay the bills, I will have all that free time to write letters to friends.

YOUR EXAMPLE OF REPETITION

1. _____

_____

_____

_____

EXAMPLE OF ANTITHESIS

We began the project full of energy and enthusiasm; we finished weary and relieved that it was over.

YOUR EXAMPLE OF ANTITHESIS

2. _____

_____

_____

_____

EXAMPLE OF INVERSION

A handy, even indispensable tool is the computer.

YOUR EXAMPLE OF INVERSION

3. _____

_____

_____

_____

ASSIGNMENT 28D STYLING SENTENCES

Using any of the structures and revision suggestions covered in Chapters 24–28, revise the following short passages to create what you feel is more varied, interesting, effective prose. You may want to write partial revisions on the passages themselves, before beginning work on the lines provided below.

1. I got off the bus. I looked for my keys. They were not in my backpack. They were not in my pocket. I remembered locking the door after me in the morning. I could not figure out where they were now. I went to the door. There were no lights on in the apartment. I rang the doorbell. My roommates were not home. I had a sinking feeling. I was locked out.

_____

_____

_____

_____

_____

2. It is really true that there is no such thing as a bargain in this day and age that we are living in
    now. Products are bought by people who have not got the time that is needed to be careful,
    smart shoppers. They are busy all the time, and money is no object to them, so high prices are
    perpetuated by the merchants, who after all cannot be blamed if they want to make a profit.

_____

_____

_____

_____

_____

_____

P A R T   V I I

Selecting Effective Words

PART VII   PREVIEW QUESTIONS

These questions are designed to help you, the student, decide what you need to study. (Answers are found at the back of the book.)

First, mark an *X* next to any of the following sentences that use language that is inappropriate for a university essay.

1. My research into the effect of television on babies requires tons of statistics.
2. Feminism and Marxism are two critical approaches frequently employed by contemporary literary critics.
3. Anyone who has studied this author's work in detail can see that he's just wrong.

Underline any words in the following sentences that seem incorrectly used or inappropriate within the context. Write in the correct word if there is an error; write *C* if there is none.

4. Woody Allen eludes to T.S. Eliot in his short stories. _____

5. The stink of baking apples was wonderfully appetizing. _____

6. I am continuously being interrupted by a continual stream of memos and phone calls.

_____

7. This wine complements the meal perfectly. _____

Respond to these questions about roots and suffixes.

8. Find two words for each of the following roots:

    a. *bio* = life (Gr.) _____

    b. *jur* or *jus* = law (Lat.) _____

9. What suffix indicates an *adverb*? _____

10. What are three suffixes indicating adjectives? _____

Use your dictionary to answer the following questions.

11. What is the origin of the word *adjudicate*? _____

12. What does *dementia praecox* mean? _____

13. Give at least two synonyms for *tendency*. _____

14. How many meanings does *revolution* have? _____

Find and correct any misspellings in the following sentences.

15. Their always telling us when they're going to have us over.
16. Harold definately never eats desert.
17. He herd the bells ringing, then he developed a headache.
18. During the rein of Queen Elizabeth I, many famous righters lived and dyed.
19. The Reagan administration concluded a nucular arms reduction treatey.

Establishing Tone

EXERCISE 29.1 VARYING TONE TO FIT YOUR AUDIENCE

Your dinner at a local sit-down restaurant kept you up all night with various physical symptoms (you decide what you ordered and what physical symptoms resulted). Using your own paper, write a complaint letter to the manager of the restaurant. In your letter, explain when and what you ate at the restaurant, and what symptoms you suffered. Be specific and detailed. End your letter by requesting a refund equal to the cost of your meal. Write this letter in a tone that will compel the manager to take you seriously but will not be considered offensive.

Next, write a letter to one of your best friends and tell that person about your meal. Be as formal or informal as you would normally be in writing to a close friend.

EXERCISE 29.2 INCREASING YOUR AWARENESS OF APPROPRIATE AND INAPPROPRIATE LANGUAGE

Describe one experience you have had with offensive language, whether you used it yourself or had it used against you. Discuss the language itself, the reason it was used, and its effect in that particular instance. Use your classmates as your audience for this discussion; select a tone appropriate to them. Begin by writing *When I think of offensive language, I think of . . . .* Finish that sentence and keep writing for at least ten minutes; write quickly, and do not worry about errors. Revise as many times as you like, paying particular attention to your tone: be sure it is appropriate to your readers and will not offend them. When you are satisfied with the tone, complete a final draft.

EXERCISE 29.3 IDENTIFYING AND USING FIGURATIVE LANGUAGE

Most of the sentences that follow contain some figurative language. In the space provided, identify the type of figurative language each sentence uses. If a sentence contains no figurative language, write *none* in the space.

EXAMPLE

By the end of her summation, Ms. Ashford had the jury following her as an orchestra follows a conductor. simile

1. The lawn cried out for water. _____

2. It's well written, but it's not exactly "To be, or not to be." _____

3. Producing broccoli, carrots, lettuce, cucumbers, even corn—the tiny garden was a produce section all by itself. _____

4. I will have to go for days without sleep in order to read all these employee evaluations. _____

5. The old radio hummed like a swarm of bees. _____

6. A whip cracking in the wind, the flag stood out, taut and rippling. _____

7. Oh, yes, I absolutely love my trips to the dentist. _____

8. "It is not cold," said the weather forecaster when announcing the temperature of 34 degrees. _____

9. With these rains and high winds and bolts of lightning, this tropical island is certainly the vacation paradise the brochure promised. _____

10. Like huge matchsticks on the horizon, the tinder-dry pines flared one by one as the flames reached them. _____

Now, on your own paper, write sentences to illustrate each of the figures of speech you have identified in this exercise (seven altogether).

EXERCISE 29.4   IDENTIFYING FAMILIAR AND INFORMAL LANGUAGE

Read the passage that follows. What characteristics would lead you to describe the passage as familiar or informal? Underline any particular words or phrases that reflect these characteristics. Then write a paragraph discussing these characteristics, using brief quotations to illustrate your points. Do you believe that the passage would be appropriate as academic writing? Why or why not?

I mean, well, pardon me but the people against Kehler are just wrong. Maybe they're airheads or something because I mean he's a nice guy. Straight arrow. He's so sincere. Look, all you have to do is watch the guy. Look at the tube, that cable channel. He's on there all the time. Besides, he's big on jobs. Wants more bucks even for the lousy ones. Heck, my kid sister works at a burger joint—she gets peanuts, $4.75, and she has to fork over for her own uniform. I heard him talking about it once—wages, I mean—and the guy *knows*. Even over the tube you could tell. He got all loud and sweaty and the crowd was cheering and all, then Benjy my stupid brother comes in and zaps it over to Mr. Dressup.

EXERCISE 29.5   REVISING FAMILIAR AND INFORMAL LANGUAGE

Using your own paper, revise the passage you examined in Exercise 29.4 so that it consistently uses formal language to establish a tone appropriate to academic writing. Begin by revising the first sentence as follows:

Opponents of the local riding candidate Kehler do not have solid grounds for argument.

EXERCISE 29.6   ANALYZING THE USE OF TECHNICAL LANGUAGE

Analyze the following passage, paying particular attention to its use of technical language. Assume that the passage is intended for the widest possible audience of university readers. Does the passage use language that will puzzle or confuse this audience? Write your analysis in a brief paragraph that itself uses the formal language appropriate to academic writing. Use your own paper for this exercise.

In 1988, the sophistication of desktop publishing software could be measured by how such software handled kerning. Some software packages adopted the strategy of consciously deleting any mention of this complicated aspect of typography. Others provided fixed kerning for a limited number of common combinations. However, the most sophisticated (and expensive) versions of this software combined WYSIWYG capabilities with the ability to custom-kern any letter combinations, thus avoiding the "widows and orphans" that plagued lesser software products.

— 30 —

Considering Diction

EXERCISE 30.1 BALANCING GENERAL AND SPECIFIC DICTION IN A PARAGRAPH

Using your own paper, follow these steps for writing a paragraph that uses both general and specific diction.

1. Select a topic from the following list.

   a) One aspect of what it is like to return to school after time away
   b) One indicator that should suggest to a student that it is time to change majors
   c) One aspect of the difficulty of moving to a new place
   d) One aspect of the joy of being a brother, sister, aunt, or uncle
   e) One memory, one fear, or one pet peeve

2. Brainstorm, freewrite, and make notes. Do not censor yourself. Save these notes for future reference.
3. Complete a rough draft; save it to compare with your final draft.
4. Revise, paying special attention to an appropriate mix of general and specific diction.
5. Write your final version.

ASSIGNMENT 30A CHOOSING LANGUAGE APPROPRIATE TO ACADEMIC ESSAYS

The sentences below contain various regional, colloquial, or slang terms. Revise the sentences to make them more acceptable for academic essays.

EXAMPLE

Some Soviet and American nukes have been junked in compliance with recent treaties.
Some Soviet and American nuclear weapons have been destroyed in compliance with recent treaties.

1. Moby Dick's humongous size was matched only by Ahab's obsessive desire to wipe him out.

   _____

   _____

2. The accused is charged with freaking out and trashing some friend's apartment.

   _____

   _____

3. This essay will zap Mr. Buckley's goofy argument.

   _____

4. Every election year, public service announcements urge us all to get on down to our respective polling stations and make our preferences known.

_____

_____

_____

5. Constance Beresford-Howe's much-loved novel, *The Book of Eve*, focuses on a 65-year-old woman and on what happens after she ditches her husband to go it alone.

_____

_____

_____

ASSIGNMENT 30B CHECKING FOR DENOTATIVE ERRORS

Read each of the following sentences, looking for denotative errors. Underline every error that you find, and write the incorrect word at the bottom of the page. When you have read all ten sentences, examine each error to determine the word intended. Write the correct word in the blank following each sentence. If there are no denotative errors in the sentence, write *C* in the blank. The first sentence has been done for you as an example. (Note: all of the correct words are to be found in the list you create at the bottom of the page.)

1. Your <u>conscious</u> would tell you that dishonesty is not the best policy.

<u>conscience</u>

2. A rabbit's foot or similar talisman gives some people the allusion of security.

_____

3. Despite the witnesses' reluctance, he did finally provide a disposition.

_____

4. Conscientious employees typically expect promotions and regular increases in compensation.

_____

5. Now that our analyses are complete, you can expect our confidential purport by the end of this month. _____

6. When emergency personnel arrived, the victim was conscience and alert.

_____

7. Encyclopedias often feature both biographical and geographical entries.

_____

8. The main report of the memo deals with staffing levels for the following year.

_____

9. One literary illusion in this poem may be referring to Arnold's "Dover Beach."

    _____

10. The consumption of squash somehow goes against my native deposition.

    _____

ASSIGNMENT 30C UNDERSTANDING CONNOTATIVE MEANINGS

Write a sentence that accurately uses the connotations associated with each word in the following pairs of similar words. If you are unsure of the connotations of a particular word, check a good dictionary.

EXAMPLE

    dance: Fred Astaire and Ginger Rogers danced in several movies.
    motion: In motion, a hummingbird's wings are a blur.

1. *crazy:* _____

   _____

   psychotic: _____

   _____

2. *cheap:* _____

   _____

   a bargain: _____

   _____

3. *spry:* _____

   _____

   nimble: _____

   _____

4. *destruction:* _____

   _____

   disposal: _____

   _____

5. *imitation:* _____

   _____

   forgery: _____

   _____

The sentences that follow contain words with strongly judgemental connotative meanings. Underline these words; then revise the sentence to make it sound more neutral.

The city's new planning scheme emphasizes economic rejuvenation as a smokescreen to obscure the real issue of over-development.

The city's new planning proposal emphasizes economic rejuvenation rather than responding directly to residents' concerns about over-development.

6. News media crackpots claim that their news reports are fair and impartial.

_____

_____

7. Pro-choice sympathizers keep screaming that a ban on abortion would drive abortion out of hospitals and into back alleys.

_____

_____

8. A mob of protesters appeared, yelling and jabbing their signs in the air.

_____

_____

9. Liberal-minded politicians keep whining about the bums, the crazies, and the lazy.

_____

_____

10. Only recently have ladies landed seats on the Supreme Court.

_____

_____

— 31 —

Working on Vocabulary

EXERCISE 31.1 USING WORD ROOTS

One word is missing from each of the following sentences. Each missing word is formed using one of the roots in the list on page 481 of the handbook. Complete each sentence by writing in the correct word.

EXAMPLE

People who wear glasses or contact lenses would not possess 20/20 <u>vision</u> without these seeing aids.

1. Before agreeing to make a movie, a director will want to read a _____.

2. A _____ is literally an example of "writing with light."

3. Narrow tires are suitable for bicycling on flat ground; fat tires are better on bumpy _____.

4. A book of writing about a person's life is called a _____.

5. Hand labour is also called _____ labour.

6. Literally, a _____ is someone who "thinks about the soul."

7. The phenomenon that lets people see things from far away is called _____.

EXERCISE 31.2 COMPOSING USING WORD ROOTS

On a separate sheet of paper, write sentences that use at least a dozen of the roots listed on page 481 of the handbook. If you can use more than one root in a sentence, do so. After each sentence, list the roots and meanings used in that sentence.

EXERCISE 31.3 USING PREFIXES AND SUFFIXES

Drawing from the prefixes listed in Chapter 31 of the handbook and the list of common roots in this exercise, construct five new words. If you are not sure your word is in fact an English word, consult your dictionary. Write the words on a separate page, and indicate the literal meaning and the common meaning. Then use the word in a short sentence. See the example following the list of common roots.

Common Roots and Meanings

-dict-, say	-phon-, sound	-vid-, -vis-, see
-vene-, come	-graph-, write	-duct-, lead
-scrib-, write	-ped-, foot	-mit-, -mis-, send

transmit   Literal meaning: *across + send*   Common meaning: *to send across*
Sentence: *A radio tower transmits radio waves.*

Attach an appropriate noun suffix to each of the following root words. Then write two sentences. Use the original word in the first sentence. Use the new word in the second sentence. Consult your dictionary as necessary.

king   *Henry VIII is a famous British king.*

kingdom
The daily changing of the guard reminds Britons that they still live in a kingdom.

1. operate   2. false   3. friend

Add an appropriate verb or adjective suffix to each of the root words that follow. Then follow the instructions given for the first three words.

4. broad   5. suspense   6. pass

EXERCISE 31.4   DETERMINING MEANING FROM CONTEXT

Find a passage in a book or magazine containing words with which you are not familiar (ask your instructor for help in choosing one if you have trouble). Read until you have found eight words that you do not know. On a separate page, copy each word and write what you think it means, based on the context, or what you can understand about the passage. Then look up the words in your dictionary to see how close you came to the correct meanings. (Note: no answer is supplied in the back of the workbook for this exercise.)

Using Dictionaries

EXERCISE 32.1 CONSULTING BASIC DICTIONARY ENTRIES

For each of the following words, consult a dictionary to confirm spelling and to determine syllabic divisions. Some of the words may be spelled incorrectly; consider possible variants before you give up! On your own paper, write the correctly spelled word, placing asterisks between the syllables. At the top of your paper, indicate the name of the dictionary you are using.

EXAMPLE

   disterbution   *dis*tri*bu*tion*

1. precede
2. hors d'eourve
3. prestigeous
4. inviegle
5. pin-head
6. manikin
7. necesary
8. meadiate
9. accuterment

Now find two or three synonyms for each of the following words.

EXAMPLE

   fair   *just, equitable, impartial*

10. material
11. demand
12. illuminate
13. way
14. angry
15. word
16. bothered
17. place
18. chilly

Finally, look up the following words. For each word, write out each pronunciation provided, indicate the grammatical functions, and briefly summarize all meanings. Note that many words have more than one meaning. Follow the format of the example.

EXAMPLE

   conduct

   Pronunciations: *kən duct' (v.), kon' duct (n.)*
   Grammatical Function Labels: *v. – tr. (transitive verb), n. (noun)*
   Meanings: *(v.) to direct the course of, lead, or manage: (n.) the way a person acts, behavior management*

19. concrete
20. delegate
21. animate
22. interest
23. converse
24. advertisement
25. advocate
26. recluse
27. amortize

EXERCISE 32.2   USING A THESAURUS

Use a thesaurus to find five synonyms for each of the italicized words in the phrases that follow. If you do not own a thesaurus, your reference librarian should be able to help you find one. List the synonyms on a separate sheet of paper, and be ready to discuss the shades of meaning that distinguish one synonym from another.

EXAMPLE

a *savvy* politician

Synonyms: *shrewd, perceptive, wise, understanding, experienced*

1. to *satiate* her hunger for knowledge
2. to *reject* all bids for the construction project
3. an *obscure* Amazonian tribe
4. to *pacify* an angry boss
5. the *strength* of her argument

EXERCISE 32.3   USING THE LIBRARY'S SPECIAL DICTIONARIES

At your local library, find special dictionaries in the reference area (ask your reference librarian for help if you need it). Select three of them. For each, on your own paper, provide the types of information shown in the example below.

EXAMPLE

Title: *The Oxford Dictionary of English Christian Names*
Author or Editor: E.G. Withycombe, ed.
Publisher: Oxford University Press
Year of Publication: 1977
Information Provided: 310 pages of first names together with their meanings and origins
Sample Entry (from p. 235): OSWIN (m): Old English *Oswin*, compound of *os* 'a god' and *wine* 'friend.' It remained in use until the 14th C. and was occasionally revived in the 19th C.

Next, consulting a dictionary of usage, briefly answer the following questions. Indicate the name, all authors or editors, and the publisher of the dictionary you consult.

EXAMPLE

What is the difference, if any, between *further* and *farther*?

Fowler's *Modern English Usage* says that *farther* is now common only where distance is concerned. *Further* "has gained a virtual monopoly of the sense of *moreover*, both alone and in the compound *furthermore*."

A Dictionary of Modern English Usage, by H.W. Fowler, 2nd ed., revised by Sir Ernest Gowers. New York: Oxford University Press (paperback), 1983, p. 190.

1. What is the difference between *libel* and *slander*?
2. Is it permissable to *allude* to someone by name?
3. What is the difference between *mendacity* and *mendicity*?

— 33 —

Mastering Spelling

EXERCISE 33.1 NOTING SPELLING UNCERTAINTIES AS YOU WRITE AND PROOFREADING FOR MISSPELLINGS

On your own paper, freewrite quickly and nonstop on the topic of diet and health. Begin by copying this opening: *When I think about diet and health, I think about* .... Finish that sentence and keep right on going. Do not worry about grammatical correctness. If you are concerned about the spelling of particular words, simply underline those words and go on.

Once you have finished freewriting, proofread your work sentence by sentence, starting with the last sentence and working toward the first. Underline any words you think may be misspelled. Then look them up, correct them, and make a list of your corrections.

EXERCISE 33.2 REVIEWING COMMONLY MISSPELLED WORDS

Reread the list of commonly misspelled words on page 500 in the handbook. Identify from the list five words that have given you trouble in the past. Indicate how you misspelled the word, and then use that word (correctly spelled) in a sentence. Use your own paper for this exercise.

EXAMPLE

Word: apparently
In the past, I've misspelled this word by adding an extra *r*.
Sentence: After checking her purse, Elvira said, "Apparently, I forgot the grocery list."

EXERCISE 33.3 DISTINGUISHING BETWEEN HOMONYMS AND OTHER SIMILAR-SOUNDING WORDS

Five pairs of words are given below. For each word, write a sentence that uses the word correctly. Use your own paper for this exercise.

EXAMPLE

a. witch b. which
a. The wicked witch wore ruby slippers.
b. I cannot decide which one of these movies to rent tonight.

1. a. lose b. loose
2. a. conscience b. conscious
3. a. descent b. dissent
4. a. accept b. except
5. a. ladder b. latter

96

Now choose five other pairs of troublesome words (refer to the words listed in the text if necessary). Use each word correctly in a sentence. Make the best use of this part of the exercise by selecting words that you know you tend to confuse.

EXERCISE 33.4   USING RULES FOR *I* BEFORE *E* AND FOR SOME SUFFIXES

Read the following five sentences carefully. Circle any misspelled words you find, and write the correct spelling above each misspelling.

EXAMPLE ~~Basicly~~ ~~procedes~~ of the fund-raising activities will be used to rebuild the ~~nieghbour's~~ house.
Basically   proceeds   neighbour's

1.   A carful analysis of the situation indicates that niether party has recieved a paycheque for last

     week.

2.   Friends can usualally help overcome greif.

3.   Children sometimes have trouble shareing toys or treating each other diplomaticly.

4.   Haveing the ceiling fixed has been a big relief.

5.   Paco is a couragous goalie who truely enjoys playing soccer.

EXERCISE 33.5   USING ADDITIONAL SUFFIX RULES

Based on the suffix rules discussed in the handbook, determine the proper spelling of the following new words and state the rule you applied. Use your own paper for this exercise.

EXAMPLE

    coin + -ed

    Correct spelling: coined
    Rule: In words of one syllable, double the final consonant only when a single vowel precedes the final consonant.

1.   employ + -er
2.   conduct + -ing
3.   refer + -ing
4.   study + -ed
5.   control + -able

ASSIGNMENT 33A   CONSTRUCTING A PERSONAL SPELLING CHART

Following the format given below, begin your own personal spelling chart. Use anything you have written recently (the draft you produced in Exercise 33.1, for instance, or a letter or a list). Find and list at least ten words you have misspelled, and fill out the other three columns of the chart for each of those words. If your draft does not contain ten misspellings, complete your chart with words you have misspelled in the past. Finally, identify and list any misspelling patterns you see in your chart—

what kinds of words should you look at more carefully the next time you are proofreading your writing for spelling errors? One common misspelling has been entered as an example. (NOTE: There is no answer supplied in the back of the workbook for this exercise.)

Word (Spelled Correctly)	Inaccurate Version	Letters or Syllables Involved	Type of Misspelling
EXAMPLE			
due	do	o/ue	homonym

ASSIGNMENT 33B PROOFREADING FOR SPELLING ERRORS

Proofread the following passage. Underline any misspelled words or words you do not know how to spell. Check all of them and then, in the space provided below, write out a list of the misspellings you found and the correct spelling of each.

Constructing any thing takes knowlege, time, and patients. Wether you are sewwing a dress, desining a cabinet, or useing your culinery skills to make a grate omelet, chances are that your product will not be prefect the first time. So plan on makeing that first dress for youself and giving the second one as a gift; plan on staying at the workbench longer than you woud like and on hanging that first cabanet in the garage; and plan on consumeing that first omelet in privite. In this way, your expectted mistakes hurt no one. Keeping your patience, maintaning high stanards, controling your tempter—these things aren't easy. However, if you can make mistakes and lern from them, your work will improove and so wil your own estimateion of your talence.

P A R T   V I I I

Using Conventional Punctuation

PART VIII   PREVIEW QUESTIONS

These questions are designed to help you, the student, decide what to study. Correct the punctuation in the following sentences. If the punctuation is already correct, write a *C* next to the sentence.

1. Even though all of their friends thought Susan and Adam shared much they did not like each other in the slightest.
2. Gina, who is my father's cousin lives in Florence.
3. The china was, totally ruined in the dishwasher.
4. The poems of Wallace Stevens are difficult at first, however, upon further reading their greatness becomes evident.
5. The restaurant advertised for all sorts of positions; short-order cook, busboys, waiters, and bartenders.
6. Whereas Andy kept calling the library a "bookhouse;" I referred to it as "the house of naps."
7. "When are we going to eat?" Marisa asked
8. P K Page entitled one of her poems "Failure at Tea."
9. "Can working with a computer really improve one's writing," they asked.
10. Just as Richard passed through customs, a guard shouted "Stop!".
11. When I read the judges decision, I decided that they had not paid sufficient attention to the defences arguments.
12. Mother does not care what the critics say, she just doesnt want to see that movie.
13. The symphony will be broadcast at eight oclock tomorrow night.
14. The dog kept a close watch on anyone who went near its supper dish.
15. I did not know that this bicycle was their's.
16. I did not know that Anne was coming with us this evening, Peter said.
17. "Eileen said that her job was "very taxing,"" Vincent reported.
18. "Cold and windy", the weather report said.
19. The police officer said that the robbers 'are now in custody.'

20. In Elizabeth Bishop's poem "Crusoe in England," she retells Defoe's novel "Robinson Crusoe."
21. A very wise person once said that there are only two types of literature; good and bad.
22. Although the wine was very good (sixty dollars worth of good), the rest of the meal was terrible.

— 34 —

Using Commas

EXERCISE 34.1   USING COMMAS AFTER INTRODUCTORY ELEMENTS

Some of the sentences in the following paragraph lack commas between introductory elements and whatever follows. Insert commas where necessary, and circle the commas you add. The first comma has been added and circled for you. For each comma you add (or decide not to add), be ready to discuss your decision.

Since its introduction by Parker Brothers in 1935ⓞMonopoly has taught several generations its unique version of capitalism. In this game of wish fulfilment everyone starts with ready cash. Decision-making is reduced to a roll of the dice. And wonder of wonders nobody works. Instead game players simply wait to arrive again at Go in order to collect another $200. Besides a life of leisure Monopoly players come to expect remarkably depressed real estate prices. For instance the Mediterranean Avenue property still sells for only $60.

EXERCISE 34.2   USING COMMAS TO SET OFF NONRESTRICTIVE INFORMATION

The following sentences contain information that is either nonrestrictive or restrictive. Read each sentence carefully and add commas as needed. Underline the nonrestrictive or restrictive element in each sentence. On the line provided, indicate whether the information you have underlined is nonrestrictive or restrictive, and indicate whether or not you have added commas.

EXAMPLES

The candidate who seems most genuine and trustworthy will get my vote.
restrictive; no commas added
Our firewood, maple and fir, should last us through the winter.
nonrestrictive; commas added

1.   The girl wearing the striped swimsuit is my daughter.

2.   We were asked to bring fruit preferably some kind of melon to the picnic.

3.   MuchMusic which is carried locally on Channel 27 features the newest in music videos.

4.   Trout that measure less than six inches must be released.

5.   Razor clams which have grown increasingly rare in recent years still make the best clam chowder.

101

EXERCISE 34.3 USING COMMAS WITH QUOTATIONS

Add needed commas to the following sentences using quotations. Circle the commas you add. Cross out any unnecessary commas.

EXAMPLE

"Showers tomorrow, with a high near 12," said the forecaster.

1. Beth said "Can we go to Beasley's after dinner?"

2. "Few Canadians" she said "are able to understand the history of conflict in Somalia."

3. People who say, "Trust me on this" always make me suspicious.

4. Pierre Trudeau appeared in a nationally televised address to declare that, he was resigning as Prime Minister.

5. "Yesterday" he said, "I disagreed with you. But after my experience today, I have changed my mind."

EXERCISE 34.4 OMITTING COMMAS BETWEEN SUBJECTS AND VERBS AND

BETWEEN VERBS AND OBJECTS

In the following passage, some sentences are punctuated correctly and some are not. Read each sentence carefully, paying close attention to the use of commas. Put an *X* through any misplaced commas. In all cases, be ready to explain your decisions.

Consider, the wonders of wood heat. The old adage is that wood heat warms you twice: once when you chop it, and once when it's burned. At our house, it seems like heating with wood provides, all sorts of warmth. Since we own neither truck nor chain saw, the first heat we get from wood, comes with the joy of stacking it. Stacking begins as soon as the wood-lot truck leaves. The process, neither intricate nor requiring excessive intelligence, involves about 120 minutes of steady movement, from woodpile in the driveway to wood stack in the garage.

ASSIGNMENT 34A USING COMMAS TO JOIN INDEPENDENT CLAUSES

Study each of the five sentences below. If commas are needed for accurate punctuation, insert them. Circle any comma you add. On the lines provided, indicate a grammatic representation of each sentence.

EXAMPLE

Before we leave for home, Alison needs to make sure the windows are tightly latched and Stefan needs to empty the refrigerator.
[Introductory element], [independent clause], and [independent clause].

1. Although we are not finished discussing this material the bell will ring soon so let me give you the assignment for tomorrow.

     _____

     _____

2. New York's subway station mosaics are true works of art and many residents of that city feel strongly that they ought to be preserved.

     _____

     _____

3. Gatineau region of Quebec boasts many kilometres of hiking and skiing trails.

     _____

     _____

4. Dad will not allow you to drive his car nor will I tell you where he hides the keys.

     _____

     _____

5. It's 28 degrees here on the porch and the rest of the family is complaining about the heat yet I like it.

     _____

     _____

ASSIGNMENT 34B USING COMMAS TO SEPARATE CO-ORDINATE ADJECTIVES AND ITEMS IN A SERIES

The sentences below contain co-ordinate adjectives, nonco-ordinate adjectives, and items in series. Add commas where needed, and circle any commas you add. On the lines provided, indicate all reasons for any commas you add. If the sentence contains any nonco-ordinate adjectives, copy them on the lines provided.

EXAMPLE

   Jane arrived carrying a doll, a lollipop, and a large crayon picture she had drawn.
   items in a series; nonco-ordinate adjectives: *large*, *crayon*

1. Beth has worn her blue Campfire hat almost nonstop since she arrived home from camp.

     _____

2. We're confronted with continuing drought a possible labour strike and the highest rate of bankruptcies in two decades.

     _____

     _____

3. The blackberry pie smelled delicious looked absolutely inviting and tasted divine.

_____

_____

4. The National Gallery in Ottawa is a dramatic original example of design that combines beauty

and utility. _____

_____

5. My father drank the beer I saved the bottles and wrote the notes and on the way home we'd throw them all off the stern end of the Borden ferry.

_____

_____

Compose your own sentences as directed below. For subject matter, think of the room in which you normally eat your meals. Make sure each sentence you write is punctuated correctly.

EXAMPLE

Write a sentence with co-ordinate adjectives and nonco-ordinate adjectives. Underline the nonco-ordinate adjectives.
The table is covered by a <u>pale blue</u> cloth fringed with intricate, expensive lace.
_____

6. Write a sentence with nonco-ordinate adjectives. Underline them.

_____

_____

7. Write a sentence with three parallel clauses. Circle any commas in the sentence.

_____

_____

8. Write a sentence with co-ordinate adjectives. Circle any commas in the sentence.

_____

_____

9. Write a sentence with only two items in a series. Circle any commas in the sentence.

_____

_____

10. Write a sentence with co-ordinate adjectives and nonco-ordinate adjectives. Underline the nonco-ordinate adjectives.

_____

_____

ASSIGNMENT 34C USING COMMAS WITH INTERJECTIONS, DIRECT ADDRESS, CONTRASTING ELEMENTS, PARENTHETICAL AND TRANSITIONAL EXPRESSIONS, TAG QUESTIONS, AND PARTS OF DATES, ADDRESSES, TITLES, AND NUMBERS

Write sentences incorporating the elements specified in each case. Make sure that your sentences use commas correctly, both for the specified elements and anywhere else they may be necessary. In each case, be ready to discuss your comma usage.

EXAMPLE

Write a sentence that includes a city and a province.
We visited the planetarium in Winnipeg, Manitoba.

1. Write a sentence that includes contrasting elements.

_____

_____

2. Write a sentence that includes a number greater than ten thousand.

_____

_____

3. Write a sentence that includes a month and year only.

_____

_____

4. Write a sentence that includes a mailing address and postal code.

_____

_____

5. Write a sentence that includes an interjection.

_____

_____

Add needed commas to the sentences below, and circle the commas you add.

EXAMPLE We were married on Sept. 11, 1971.

6. Rak could you read over the third paragraph and tell me what it says to you?
7. Laura Williams M.D. can be found in office 228 on the second floor.
8. Now we stitch the seam right?
9. Last year I am sorry to say six elms had to be destroyed due to Dutch elm disease.
10. Your rough draft is due Friday October 28.

ASSIGNMENT 34D DISTINGUISHING BETWEEN RESTRICTIVE AND NONRESTRICTIVE SENTENCE ELEMENTS

Underline the restrictive or nonrestrictive elements in each of the following sentences. Indicate whether the material you have underlined is restrictive or nonrestrictive. Punctuate the sentence correctly, and circle any commas you add.

EXAMPLES

The lab technician reports that the blood tests⊙which were performed yesterday⊙were negative. nonrestrictive
The lab technician reports that the blood tests that were performed yesterday were negative. restrictive

1. Pit bulls that have been mistreated by their owners are often hostile to anyone who gets too close. _____

2. The furniture marked down for this special sale is going fast. _____

3. The evacuees some with only the clothes on their backs prepared to spend the night inside the high school gym. _____

4. The Russ Feller who is an accomplished poet and teacher lives in Kitchener, Ontario. _____

5. Health care administration a field that has grown in recent years often attracts some of the best and brightest talents. _____

ASSIGNMENT 34E OMITTING UNNECESSARY COMMAS

Cross out any unnecessary commas in the following sentences. If a sentence is correct as shown, write *C* next to its number.

EXAMPLE

For twenty-six straight days, the high temperature in Saskatoon✗reached over thirty degrees.

1. During midsummer one year, (on the fourth of July, in fact) snow fell in Missoula.
2. Nothing smells more delicious, than a field of ripe strawberries waiting to be picked.
3. Raspberries make, for great pies, and, sweet jelly.
4. Jim runs fifteen kilometres every other day, and he says he feels strong, healthy, and fit.
5. Two lanes (usually those on the far left side of the pool), are routinely reserved for lap swimming.
6. Any list of living, well-respected short story writers would have to include Mavis Gallant, Ellen Gilchrist, and Alice Munro, (the queen of them all).

ASSIGNMENT 34F USING COMMAS CORRECTLY

The following sentences are punctuated correctly. Combine or revise each according to the specific directions. Make sure your new version is punctuated accurately.

EXAMPLE

My father graduated from Louisbourg High School in 1933. (Revise so that the sentence begins *In 1933 . . .*)
In 1933, my father graduated from Louisbourg High School.

1. Carpentry requires patience, as does needlework. (Revise so that the sentence subjects are *carpentry* and *needlework*.) _____

_____

2. Designing your own clothes is not as hard as some people think. Designing your own clothes can be quite rewarding. (Combine into one sentence containing secondary, nonrestrictive information.)

_____

_____

3. Some writers like to read a bit before writing. Some writers make copious notes to themselves. Some writers are too terrified to do anything. Some writers just sit down and start writing whatever comes to mind. (Combine into one sentence with multiple independent clauses.) _____

_____

_____

4. You wake up in Vancouver. You look out the window. It's so clear that you understand why everyone moved here. This happens on those April mornings after a heavy rain. (Combine into one sentence with an introductory element followed by several independent clauses.) _____

_____

_____

5. These orientation classes are designed for transfer students only. These orientation classes begin Monday morning at 9:00. (Revise to a single sentence containing restrictive information.) _____

_____

On the lines provided, combine each of the following groups of sentences into one sentence of connected independent clauses. Join the independent clauses by using commas and appropriate coordinating conjunctions. Use pronouns as necessary.

EXAMPLE

Hay fever season has arrived. We had better buy more Kleenex.
Hay fever season has arrived, so we had better buy more Kleenex.

6. The typewriter is fast. The typewriter produces professional-looking documents.

_____

107

7. The typewriter is fast. The typewriter produces professional-looking documents. I still prefer to handwrite my memos. _____

_____

8. We have confirmed our reservations. We have taken the dog to the neighbours'. The car is packed. Let's go. _____

_____

9. Margaret tripped going down the stairs. She did not lose consciousness.

_____

10. You love golf. You enjoy the companionship. You admire the lush landscape. You play maybe once a year. _____

_____

Using Semicolons

EXERCISE 35.1 REVISING USING SEMICOLONS

Some of the sentences in the passage that follows are punctuated inaccurately. Others may be accurate in their punctuation, but you may not feel the current version to be the most effective one. Edit the passage, making whatever minor revisions you feel necessary. Copy your best version on your own paper, and make sure that your version is punctuated accurately. Also make sure that your revised version uses semicolons in at least three instances. Finally, underline your changes.

Recovering alcoholics are some of the nicest people you'd ever want to meet, unfortunately, they also tell some of the saddest, most distressing stories. Many of them come from alcoholic families maybe the father was a functional, low-profile drinker for years; maybe the mother drank during the day and locked her own kids out of the house because she couldn't stand their noise; maybe the kids also suffered from sexual abuse or other physical violence; when these kids reached adulthood, they hid their hurt in a bottle. Some of them didn't wait for adulthood. Some drank right along with their parents.

Untreated alcoholics believe they have every reason to drink. Through treatment, however, they come to learn that no reason is a good enough reason for them to drink. For the alcoholic, that beer or wine or gin makes every problem worse, without fail, excessive, compulsive drinking creates new problems. Staying clean and sober doesn't do away with the alcoholic's problems; it does eliminate one pressing, overpowering difficulty, the sober alcoholic then has at least the opportunity to deal with other problems. Recovery isn't easy. Recovery is never complete. But with family support and the help of organizations like Alcoholics Anonymous, people do dry out, families do get better.

ASSIGNMENT 35A USING SEMICOLONS TO LINK INDEPENDENT CLAUSES

Carefully check the punctuation in the following sentences. If the punctuation is accurate, write *C* on the lines provided. If it is inaccurate, write a corrected version.

EXAMPLE

The unwanted package arrived C.O.D., I politely refused to pay the charges.
The unwanted package arrived C.O.D.; I politely refused to pay the charges.

1. The traffic safety office has mailed out forms to request parking stickers; completed forms are due back by October 1. _____

   _____

2. My current work-study job ends in two weeks. I'll need to find a new position; starting next term. _____

   _____

3. Please save your questions for the end of the presentation; if you don't understand.

   _____

4. For four glorious but underpaid weeks; I'll be working in Jasper this summer.

   _____

5. Swinging the door open quietly; the two police officers surprised a young burglar as he worked; to disconnect the cable wire from the Tuckers' colour television. _____

   _____

   _____

6. The invitation distinctly said R.S.V.P., even so, we lost the invitation and never properly responded. _____

   _____

7. Monday's U.S. Open tennis tournament was rained out, however, play is scheduled to resume Tuesday. _____

   _____

8. Oak burns slowly and makes a hot fire; fir splits easily and makes superior kindling. _____

   _____

9. Raspberries, which are my favourite fresh fruit, ripen in late June and early July in addition, some years there's a later, smaller crop in September. _____

   _____

   _____

Use a semicolon and whatever other punctuation is required to combine each of the following sets of brief sentences into one longer sentence. You may revise the sentences slightly as needed. Make sure that your new sentence is punctuated correctly.

EXAMPLE

> We walked the dog after dinner. The moon rose. The moon shone round and white as a bone china saucer. While we were walking the dog after dinner, the moon rose; it shone round and white as a bone china saucer.

10. A replacement key for your office costs $10. You might lose your office key. Lost keys are sometimes turned in at the front security desk.

11. Some people think of wallpaper hanging as a do-it-yourself project. We tried wallpaper hanging. We think of wallpaper hanging as a project for professionals only.

12. I'll meet your train at the downtown station. Look for the woman under a dark blue umbrella. I'll also be carrying a tan briefcase.

13. There are fewer drive-in theatres than there once were. The Imperial Drive-in, for example, has been demolished for a shopping mall.

Using End Punctuation

EXERCISE 36.1   USING PERIODS TO SIGNAL THE ENDS OF SENTENCES

Read this paragraph:

Without periods and the spaces that conventionally follow them, readers would have no ready way of recognizing the end of a sentence instead of being able to read quickly and effortlessly, we would all be required to slow down and continually ask ourselves whether or not the words we have just read constitute a complete sentence in short, we would be analyzing the form of the writing as well as trying to grasp its content; we would be doing two things at once chances are we would not be entirely successful with either task the end result would be frustration and an unwillingness to read

Now go back and reread the paragraph, putting in a period every time you think you have come to the end of a sentence. Does reading the paragraph feel easier and more comfortable now?

EXERCISE 36.2   PROOFREADING AND REVISING END-PUNCTUATION ERRORS

Proofread the following passage for errors with end punctuation (periods, question marks, and exclamation points). Add needed end punctuation, and make sure that every new sentence begins with a capital letter. Cross out any punctuation that should not be there. If you are not sure whether to use periods with particular abbreviations, consult your dictionary.

Most people think of jogging as a solitary activity I'll grant that most of the time it is exactly that. But occasionally something unusual happens. Once a Winnebago with strange licence plates swerved across the centre line and stopped right in front of me? I swerved too, trying not to break stride, only to hear a rather shrill voice yell "Wait a minute, honey hey we need to talk to you. I stopped I can't help it if my parents taught me to be polite "Son," the driver said, "we're touring Canada, and I'm afraid we're just a little bit lost". As it turned out, they were looking for an address in the southeastern part of town; however, they were driving around on streets all clearly labelled as northwest they never noticed (or at least never acknowledged) that I was beet red in the face, sweaty, and scowling. I suppose they figured they were being polite, too.

Another time a kid with a flat bicycle tire ran along beside me for fifty metres or so, saying, "Mister, you got ten dollars I can borrow. My tire's flat you got a dime so I can call my mom." He didn't notice that my jogging shorts had no pockets. Of course, when I got home and told my kids about the bicycle rider's plight, they could hardly believe it "Did that guy really expect you to have ten dollars, one asked? And said the other, "Did he really think you'd give it to him even if you had it"? All I could do was answer with a shrug. I hadn't taken the requests too seriously. I'd been too busy trying to breathe on a regular basis.

ASSIGNMENT 36A   IDENTIFYING AND CORRECTING END-PUNCTUATION ERRORS

Some of the following sentences use question marks correctly, but many do not. Proofread each sentence. If the printed version is accurate, write *C* on the lines provided. If the printed version needs correction, copy the sentence with corrected punctuation on the lines.

Can you please clean up your room before I lose my temper.
Can you please clean up your room before I lose my temper?

1. Didn't I say? "Either clean up your room, or there'll be no dessert after dinner?"

   _____

   _____

2. Was it in sixth grade that we first studied Canadian history or fifth grade?

   _____

   _____

3. If you're not sure which bus to ride, just ask the driver if the bus is going to the Kanata

   area. _____

   _____

4. "Have you heard the one about the tourist and the barber," he asked.

   _____

   _____

5. Did you just say, "What time is it?"

   _____

6. "Yes, I asked you what time it was?"

   _____

7. "Olga, did Beth invite you over after school" she asked?

   _____

8. "Have you arranged for a substitute so that we can go to the hockey game tonight?" asked

   Dennis. _____

   _____

9. My opponent has posed an interesting question: "Should Canada just become a neutral country

   like Switzerland"? _____

   _____

   _____

10. Displaying uncommon impatience, she hollered, "Why is our food so slow?"

    _____

    _____

11. What, exactly, do you want!

_____

12. What do you mean by coming in here and telling me to leave the room.

_____

— 37 —

Using Apostrophes

ASSIGNMENT 37A USING APOSTROPHES TO SIGNAL POSSESSION

The following sentences contain material in parentheses. Incorporate that material, using apostrophes correctly.

EXAMPLE

Many of the street signs (found in Pugwash) are in both English and Gaelic.
Many of Pugwash's street signs are in both English and Gaelic.

1. The guy wires (belonging to the antenna) were snapped by the wind.

   _____

2. (The dresses belonging to your children) look very pretty.

   _____

3. The poster (advertising the Stratford Festival) hung on his wall.

   _____

4. The finish (belonging to the piano) was cracked and peeling.

   _____

5. Let's order another box of ribbons (that our typewriters use).

   _____

6. (The poster made by Sean and the poster made by Janet) have both been chosen as winners.

   _____

7. It sounds like your muffler (which is part of your station wagon) needs to be replaced.

   _____

8. (The paint that belongs to it) was scratched in the accident.

   _____

9. (The choices of all participating voters) have been made.

   _____

10. (The paper belonging to me) was turned in on time.

    _____

115

11. (It is) an important decision.

_____

12. Yes, I think (that is) (the coat belonging to him) over there on the chair. _____

_____

ASSIGNMENT 37B USING APOSTROPHES TO CREATE CONTRACTIONS

Read each sentence below. If the sentence uses contractions, rewrite it so that it uses full forms. If the sentence uses full forms, rewrite it so that it uses contractions. Correct any improperly used contractions. Think about the sentence's meaning and its probable context. Then indicate which of the two forms of the sentence you consider more appropriate by placing an _X_ next to it.

EXAMPLE

In the unlikely event of any accidental injury to your child, medical personnel'll be available immediately.
In the unlikely event of any accidental injury to your child, medical personnel will be available immediately. **X**

1. Should not we have stopped at the market for more milk?

_____

2. You have been listening to several people as they have described how the United Way has helped them; now will you not please take out your chequebooks and help your neighbours?

_____

_____

_____

3. That guy who's been giving you a ride after class called at about nine o'clock.

_____

_____

4. Some critics argue that Timothy Findley'll be remembered as one of the best novelists of the 1980s. _____

_____

5. The clothes I am washing now did not really get too dirty.

_____

6. For the test you'll be taking on Monday, your required to have a pencil with a No. 2 lead. _____

_____

7. The judge'll be available to meet with you once court adjourns.

_____

8. The distributor informs me that you're order has not received it's required approval from the business office.

_____

_____

9. Who's ever responsible for an accident has the legal obligation to compensate any injured

parties. _____

_____

10. You've been told over and over that you shouldn't play in the street.

_____

ASSIGNMENT 37C USING APOSTROPHES

The following passage contains numerous errors involving apostrophes. Circle any errors you find, and pencil in your corrections in the spaces between lines.

With the end of summer, many students begin to think about registration for the new term, course schedule booklets become hot items, and the rumour mill churns into operation. Whose had whom in which classes? Hows so and so in history? How many As did so and so give in psychology last term? Anyone heard how many essays there'll be? Hallways buzz and the tables in the student union fill up once more. All over campus, department secretaries patience wears thin even as they politely answer question's about adding or dropping classes, changing majors, and so forth. Faculty members offices echo with the sound of typewriters or computer printers. Meanwhile, the bookstores lines stretch back from the cash registers all the way to the next years calendars, which are already on sale. Returning student's sometimes find its not possible to walk across campus without running into an old acquaintance. They keep "Hows it going?" and "What's new?" on the tip of the tongue.

By late November, the trees dont rustle; theyre bare. Maybe its even snowed already. Snow or not, much of the terms earlier anticipation has been replaced by some quite specific challenges; the paper due tomorrow, the necessary B on the next test (after two Cs and a C−), the upcoming oral presentation in French. But in August or September, all thats in the future. The sun shines, the summers moneys in the bank, and everyone secretly believes that again this term the registrars computer will be friendly.

— 38 —

Using Quotation Marks

EXERCISE 38.1 VARYING QUOTATION FORMAT ACCORDING TO LENGTH

Find a poem that you particularly like. Read the poem and decide on the one or two lines you like best. Use a sentence or two to introduce those lines, and then quote them. Punctuate your writing and your quotation accurately. Type your work, double-spaced, or write it out carefully on your own paper.

EXAMPLE

Andrew Marvell's "To His Coy Mistress" is one of the few poems that I have memorized. My favourite lines come at the very end: "Thus, though we cannot make our sun / Stand still, yet we will make him run."

Find a paragraph in the handbook that is longer than five lines and has been helpful to you. Introduce the paragraph by telling why it has been helpful; then quote the paragraph itself. Make sure that your block quotation follows the guidelines set forth in Chapter 38. Make sure that your introduction to the quotation indicates the original page number of your quoted material. Type your work, double-spaced, or write it out carefully on your own paper.

EXERCISE 38.2 USING QUOTATION MARKS TO SIGNAL DIALOGUE

Using your own paper, write a short (one to two pages) fictional sketch that features dialogue between two characters. Use quotation marks accurately, and use new paragraphs to indicate the shift from one speaker to the other.

ASSIGNMENT 38A USING QUOTATION MARKS TO SIGNAL DIRECT QUOTATION

Copy the sentences below, using quotation marks each time someone else's exact words are being used. Make sure that you use quotation marks with other punctuation marks correctly.

EXAMPLE

Your phone's ringing! yelled Phil from the end of the hall.
"Your phone's ringing!" yelled Phil from the end of the hall.

1. Ultimately, our differences with management may result in the need to strike; the crowd shifted uneasily at those words.

2. I'm going outside for some fresh air, said Barb as she put on her sweater, but I'll only be a few minutes.

_____

_____

3. Has everyone been informed that Ms. Jenkins said, For the duration of these training seminars, there will be no absences?

_____

_____

4. I could not believe the condition of my hometown, he wrote.

_____

_____

5. Oscar Wilde didn't say The shallow never know themselves; he said, Only the shallow know themselves.

_____

_____

Read the following sentences. On the line, identify the quotation as either direct or indirect. Add quotation marks as needed.

EXAMPLE

It was a critic in *Saturday Review* who wrote of Dickens, "We do not believe in the permanence of his reputation." <u>direct</u>

6. Through his publicist, Michael Jackson said that he was pleased at the support his Japanese fans had shown him. _____

7. After a tornado ripped through her house, a tearful Alberta woman said We're here today only because God held us in his hand; that's all I can say. _____

8. The Beast destroyed my brief peace is the first sentence of Guy Vanderhaeghe's *My Present Age*. _____

9. Most people like to characterize themselves as open-minded and flexible enough to change when the circumstances demand. _____

10. The local employment office's annual summary states that the current unemployment rate is 1.3 percent lower than it was five years ago. _____

ASSIGNMENT 38B   USING QUOTATION MARKS CORRECTLY

Proofread the following sentences for correct use of quotation marks. If the sentence is correct, write

C on the lines provided. If the sentence needs to be repunctuated, copy the sentence and punctuate it accurately.

EXAMPLE

> "Meeting of Strangers and Tea at My Shetland Aunt's" remain two of his favourite Earle Birney poems.
> "Meeting of Strangers" and "Tea at My Shetland Aunt's" remain two of his favourite Earle Birney poems.

1. Listen," screamed the television character, if you say I'm going to leave you" one more time, I'll ask you to leave!

_____

_____

2. George Orwell's essay "Politics and the English Language deserves its place in the anthologies.

_____

_____

3. The episode I enjoyed most,' she said, was the one titled "Atomic Shakespeare; it was inventive and funny.

_____

_____

4. 'Buddhist Economics is not a chapter title you'll find in too many textbooks.'

_____

_____

5. "As I was telling you, he sat there in his library, sipped his drink, and said, I find it delightfully reassuring to live among all these words."

_____

_____

6. "Who but the British," the guide remarked, "would knit 'sweaters' for their teapots?"

_____

_____

7. "Did I tell you," he said, that when Cary got here, the first thing she asked was 'Well, are the hills alive with the sound of music"?

_____

_____

8. The opening line of her parody read, "It was Pee-wee Herman who said 'Give me liberty, but not bad breath.

_____

_____

9. When it came to family pets, the exterminators' contract specifically denied any responsibility for their safety.

    _____

    _____

    _____

10. The medical report came to this conclusion: "Patients who 'take responsibility for their own recovery' do indeed recover faster than those who see themselves as victims passively accepting treatment."

    _____

    _____

    _____

    _____

ASSIGNMENT 38C   IDENTIFYING AND CORRECTING ERRORS WITH QUOTATION MARKS

Below is the final draft of a brief essay. Read it first. Then proofread it for errors involving quotation marks. Place a check in the left margin beside any line that needs correction. Cross out whatever should not be there; add whatever should. If some portion of the essay needs repositioning, indicate that in the margin.

One of the best kept secrets about poetry is that reading it can be a wonderful, benign addiction. Poems, like anything else handmade, reflect their makers; they are as strange, exotic, thought-provoking, and beautiful as people. Who can deny a rush of adrenaline at taking a deep breath (a really deep breath) and saying (almost singing) some of the most gorgeous sounds in English: "Now as I was young and easy under the apple boughs / About the lilting house and happy as the grass was green, / The night above the dingle starry, / Time let me hail and climb /

> Golden in the heydays of his eyes,
> And honoured among wagons I was prince of the apple towns
> And once below a time I lordly had the trees and leaves
> Trail with daisies and barley
> Down the rivers of the windfall light."

So goes the opening stanza of Dylan Thomas's Fern Hill. Skeptics might say "Even if we grant that the language of Fern Hill is indeed gorgeous, as you say, it is also virtually impossible to follow.

Ah, pity the skeptics; they have an adversarial relationship with the world. Fern Hill is difficult only for readers who ask that it transmit its content as a newspaper does. Newspapers are read for their information. They're written to be read easily, quickly. The sentences are short, and individually they are forgettable. Who recalls last week's headlines? In contrast, Poetry, said Ezra Pound, is news that stays news.

The truth is, Fern Hill is made to be read slowly and even inquisitively. How, after all, can a house be called "lilting"? The word has more to do with song than with architecture. Could someone have been singing? How happy is happy as the grass was green? It's as happy as the night is starry. Is the pun on heydays (hay days) intentional? What can it mean to be prince of the apple towns? Could apple towns be rows of apple trees—an orchard? Does that tie in with the "windfall" of the last line?

And what does this add up to? Doesn't it add up to an intensity of feeling that makes the experience ours even though it's not? We don't know that farm, except we do. We've seen the imaginations of children; we've seen how they become queens or kings of their bedrooms, their toys, their dolls. The speaker in Fern Hill is prince of it all. The speaker owned that farm, that time, and owns it still.

What about the odd shape of Fern Hill on the page? Why insist on such an arrangement? Why is the second stanza arranged identically to the first? And how is it that Thomas could ensure that the first line of the second

121

stanza contains precisely the same number of syllables as the first line of the first stanza? The same correspondence is true for the second lines of each stanza, and the third lines, and so on until the fifth stanza, which changes the pattern somewhat. What astonishing union of content and form are we looking at here?

Actually, Fern Hill is childhood distilled; all the frustrations and angers have been boiled away. What's left is an awe-inspiring precision of language and feeling. What's left is the exhilaration of childhood as time in the Garden of Eden, 'it was all / Shining, it was Adam and maiden, / The sky gathered again / And the sun grew round that very day.' If poems are indeed an addiction, they must be the very best kind.

Using Other Punctuation Marks

EXERCISE 39.1 USING PARENTHESES AND BRACKETS

Some of the five sentences that follow confuse parentheses and brackets. If a sentence uses these punctuation marks correctly, write *C* in the margin next to it. If the sentence uses these punctuation marks incorrectly, write in the necessary corrections.

EXAMPLE

"I think he [Robinson Jeffers] thought of people as wild, passionate, and usually not very rational or altruistic," Alfred said. (Note: Assume that the name did not form part of the quotation and was inserted by the writer reporting this opinion.)

1. That mantel clock [made in Germany in 1888] has been in the family since my father's grandmother brought it over with her in 1901.
2. Either [1] we propose our modifications now, or (2) we wait for the final set of engineering results and risk a production failure.
3. "Your presentation (which was, by the way, cogently argued) impressed several members of the committee." (Assume that the same speaker said all of these words.)
4. Touring the Fortress of Louisbourg [in Cape Breton, Nova Scotia] gives you an idea of how French settlers lived in the mid-eighteenth century.
5. "Her book [*Out of Africa*] is to me both an astonishment and a delight." (Assume that the title has been inserted and was not part of the original quotation.)

EXERCISE 39.2 REVISING TO ENSURE CORRECT USE OF PARENTHESES

In each of the two passages that follow, parentheses have been overused or used inappropriately. Using your own paper, rewrite each passage so that parentheses are used sparingly and appropriately, making sure that crucial information does not appear in parentheses.

1. *Chatelaine* magazine has named Brandon (Manitoba) one of the ten best Canadian cities to live in. Although it does not boast high salaries (on average), Brandon does have a low unemployment rate (5.9 percent) and an attractive cost of living (for example, $75 000 buys a new three-bedroom bungalow). With a population of around 40 000, Brandon is a small city (which contributes to the sense of community that residents enjoy). It has exceptional recreational facilities for a city its size (because the Canada Winter Games were held there in 1979). Brandon University's school of music and the arts centre (recently built downtown) both contribute to the cultural flavour of this appealing city.
2. Our car was approaching the intersection from the west (we were arguing about which movie we were going to see, so maybe we weren't paying close attention) when somebody (maybe Judy, who was driving) yelled "No!" Just seconds after that (I think by then Judy had begun to swerve right to try to get out of the way), the station wagon hit our front end behind the wheel (the left one). As metal crunched and we spun around, it all seemed to be happening in slow motion.

ASSIGNMENT 39A   USING DASHES

Read the sentences below, paying particular attention to the use of dashes. If the sentence is acceptable as written, write *C* on the lines. If the sentence needs revising, write your revision on the lines. Make sure your revision uses dashes correctly. Be ready to explain your reasoning.

EXAMPLE

Hamburg today the largest city—and busiest port—in West Germany—has twice risen from the ashes of fire and destruction.
Hamburg—today the largest city and busiest port in West Germany—has twice risen from the ashes of fire and destruction.

1. Few recognize the name Sarah Josepha Hale many know her poem entitled—"Mary Had a Little Lamb."

2. Several kinds of lace among them Alencon, Honiton, and Maltese—take their names from their place of origin.

3. We'll send a postcard when we arrive in Banff if we remember.

4. Their sophistication, their perceptual abilities, even how they feel about themselves children's pictures can tell us much—about the children who drew them.

5. Your papers should be finished the deadline is Friday at noon and placed in the envelope in Professor Cook's office door.

Combine each group of short sentences, using dashes appropriately as needed.

EXAMPLE

Chicago's Sears Tower contains 110 stories. It rises to a height of almost 1500 feet. It measures 104 feet taller than New York's World Trade Center. It is the world's tallest building.
Rising some 1500 feet, containing 110 stories, and measuring 104 feet taller than New York's World Trade Center—Chicago's Sears Tower is the world's tallest building.

6. Paul Klee was a renowned graphic artist, painter, and art theorist. He died some fifty years ago. He remains an influential presence for contemporary artists.

_____

_____

_____

7. Parents should act like parents. They should not act like squabbling children.

_____

_____

8. Twice Sir John A. Macdonald served as Prime Minister of Canada. This occurred from 1867 to 1873 and again from 1878 to 1891.

_____

_____

9. Renata Scotto is famous. She is an opera singer. She was born in Italy. She is still remembered for her debut in Milan in 1953. She is particularly recognized today for her performances of Puccini's *Madame Butterfly*.

_____

_____

_____

10. You should escape your troubles. You should travel without ever leaving your chair. You should save your money. You should visit your local library. You should read.

_____

_____

_____

ASSIGNMENT 39B USING COLONS

Combine the following sentences, using colons in each one. There may be more than one way to combine these sentences; for this exercise, however, make sure that your versions use colons.

EXAMPLE

Check the *Encyclopaedia Britannica*. The volume to check is volume 3. The page number is 187.
Check the *Encyclopaedia Britannica 3:187.*

1. You're supposed to bring the condiments. You ought to bring mustard, ketchup, relish, dill pickles, and mayonnaise. _____

_____

_____

2. Bill's decision was a difficult one, but he stuck to it. Bill quit smoking for good.

_____

_____

3. Judith Fingard wrote a book. It is entitled *Jack in Port*. It is subtitled *Sailortowns of Eastern Canada*. _____

_____

4. I like the Book of Proverbs. I especially like Chapter 12. I especially like verse 8 in that chapter.

_____

_____

5. The scout troop packed what seemed like a ton of gear into the van. They packed four tents, a dozen sleeping bags, three propane stoves (with propane bottles), food for two nights, ropes, craft projects, and the troop flag. _____

_____

_____

_____

Read each of the sentences below, paying particular attention to the use of colons. If the sentence is punctuated accurately, write *C* on the lines. If the sentence needs revising, write your revision on the lines. Make sure your revision uses colons correctly.

EXAMPLE

Advertisers assume that we all want to be: beautiful, protected, stylish, and trendy.
Advertisers assume that we all want to be beautiful, protected, stylish, and trendy.

6. Leonid Telyatnikov has done something he hopes no one else will have to do he has: commanded a fire crew attempting to extinguish a nuclear reactor fire.

_____

_____

_____

7. Insomniacs who turn to late-night TV for company will likely find programs on: investing in real estate, quitting smoking, and thinking positively.

_____

_____

_____

8. The list of Norman Jewison's movie credits includes: *Moonstruck*, *Fiddler on the Roof*, *Agnes of God*, and *The Cincinnati Kid*.

_____

9. The paperback mystery I bought yesterday met with an undignified end: it fell with a "plop" into the bath water.

10. Ukrainian-Canadians have traditionally made coloured or decorated eggs to celebrate: Easter and rebirth and to have on hand as gifts for visitors.

11. We ask that you come to the test equipped with the following. At least two sharpened HB pencils, erasers, two notebooks, and scrap paper.

12. Let me just tell you this, he will not come because he disapproves of the entire outing.

13. I am: annoyed, exasperated, sorely tried, and: fed up.

ASSIGNMENT 39C USING ELLIPSES

The following passage is taken from *The Coming of Winter* by David Adams Richards (Ottawa: Oberon Press, 1974). In this passage, the main character, who has been out hunting with little success, has just shot a cow. Read the passage, then copy it, leaving out the underlined portions. Make sure you use ellipses accurately.

He stood in the open field, the wind at his back, the brightness of the coloured day surrounding him, the strong flavour of autumn once again. The cow lay on its side, trying to jerk upright every so often, falling to its side again, kicking its thick hind legs. It was bleeding very little. Perhaps it didn't notice he was there. Another cow stood a short distance away watching, not venturing any closer, its enormous eyes watching. He felt sick as he fired, shaking, uncertain of his aim. And he fired four times rapidly and then only live nerves twitching in a dead hide and everything was quiet. He cursed and he could not stop shaking, could not stop feeling sick. But he felt he must leave it there, forget it. And then he laughed nervously as he turned away.

PART IX

Using Conventional Mechanics

40   Using Capitals

41   Using Abbreviations and Numbers

42   Using Italics

43   Using Hyphens

PART IX   PREVIEW QUESTIONS

These questions are designed to help you, the student, decide what to study. Correct any mistakes in capitalization, abbreviation, use of numbers, use of italics, or hyphenation that you find in the following sentences. If there are no mistakes, mark a *C* next to the sentence.

1. we will be going to Northwestern France in two weeks.
2. These books—They all cost under a dollar—are available inside.
3. James McCracken, president of a local real estate firm, ran for mayor.
4. We used to live on First Avenue, but then we moved uptown.
5. A common misconception among students is that the renaissance was man-centred whereas the middle ages were God-centred.
6. Anne Fisher is a doctor and an M.D.
7. First Kay got her B.A., then she decided to become a social worker so she applied for an M.S.W.
8. Boethius composed the *Consolation of Philosophy* somewhere between 480 and 524 AD.
9. Whenever you go to Jane's Bakery, you must take a #.
10. My parents live in Nfld., but I now go to school in Ont.
11. 6 people came to hear the lecture.
12. He has about 10,000 records.
13. The *Hebrew Bible*, the *Gospels*, and the *Koran* are all sacred books.
14. Stephen Greenblatt's chapter on "King Lear," "Shakespeare and the Exorcists," appears in his book "Shakespearean Negotiations."
15. Robert Desrosiers's dance collage, *Avalanche*, will be performed next week.
16. Every night I tune my radio to CBC and listen to *A Little Night Music*.
17. Spenser's epic, *The Fairie Queene*, begins "in medias res," in the middle of things.
18. In the Renaissance, "poetry" did not just mean verse, but all fiction.
19. "Annie Hall" is my favourite Woody Allen film.
20. Although Beethoven wrote many works for piano, his Moonlight Sonata is the best-known.
21. We depend upon oil for approximately seventy-five percent of our energy.
22. Although they said that it would be cloud-less, it rain-ed all afternoon.
23. He was always such a happy-go-lucky person.

24. None of the television stations had better-coverage of the election.
25. Only one-third of the class showed up today.
26. This anthology contains poetry from eighteenth- and nineteenth-century manuscripts.

— 40 —

Using Capitals

EXERCISE 40.1 USING CAPITALIZATION FOR THE FIRST WORD OF A NEW SENTENCE

The following passage sometimes uses capitalization incorrectly. Capitalize any words that should be capitalized, and substitute lowercase letters where necessary. Make your revisions in the spaces above the lines. The sentences are numbered for easier reference.

Basically, she was shy.[1] as a child, she had always been quite a bit shorter than her classmates, Leading to a certain amount of teasing.[2] Sometimes the teasing was quite severe — Once a dozen or more of her fifth-grade class had circled her, chanting "you're short, you're short, you're short."[3] when the playground monitor broke up the circle, She was on her knees in the middle of the group, tears on her face, Her hands held tight over her ears.[4] "no, no, no, no," She'd been screaming, trying to outshout her tormentors.[5]

Then, in eighth grade, finally she grew: she grew six inches in six months, she gained fifteen pounds, and the teasing stopped.[6] her classmates quickly forgot about it, but she did not forget.[7] for years, she had to teach herself to join the group.[8] She had to persuade herself that she would be accepted, not teased.[9] How do I know this?[10] i am that girl, or rather she is a part of me.[11] And if I am no longer shy, It is because I have worked hard.[12] I don't want to forget those experiences.[13] I do want to keep them in perspective, To learn from them rather than be victimized by them.[14]

EXERCISE 40.2 USING CAPITALS FOR PROPER NOUNS AND PROPER ADJECTIVES

Words are underlined in each of the sentences that follow. Analyse how each underlined word is used, and decide whether it should be capitalized. Then rewrite each sentence so that it uses capitalization accurately. Write your analyses and your revised sentences on a separate sheet of paper.

1. Saint John, new Brunswick, lies on the Saint John river and boasts a Population of over 80 000.
2. Screen Actress and later Princess of Monaco, Grace Kelly died when her car (which was headed North) left the road and plunged down an embankment.
3. Ottawa area Business leaders consider bell northern research one of the Region's most important corporations.

EXERCISE 40.3 MORE PRACTICE WITH CAPITALIZING PROPER NOUNS AND PROPER ADJECTIVES

Some italicized words in the following sentences are capitalized; others are not. Analyse how each italicized word is used, and briefly note that analysis as shown below. Then rewrite the sentence so that it uses capitalization accurately.

EXAMPLE

> That *Botany* 201 *class* looks tough, but not as tough as *french* or *physics*.
> *Botany*: title of actual class; capitalize
> *class*: not part of a title; do not capitalize
> *french*: name of a language; capitalize
> *physics*: not the title of a specific course; do not capitalize
> Revision: That Botany 201 class looks tough, but not as tough as French or physics.

1. Many non-natives are surprised by the rent *Landlords* typically charge for *A Toronto Apartment*.
2. *The Division Of* Language and Literature is happy to announce that it is the recipient of a grant from the Ontario Ministry of *education*.
3. Cub *scouts*, Rotarians, members of the Junior Service *league*, and *Members* of various *University* clubs joined forces yesterday to publicize the need for more blood donations.
4. Since *Remembrance* Day falls on *a saturday* this *year*, the actual observance will be reserved for the following Monday.
5. The *biblical* injunction to *honour* one's parents is echoed in *the koran* and can also be found in the *various* sayings attributed to *Confucius*.

ASSIGNMENT 40A REVISING FOR CORRECT CAPITALIZATION

In the following sentences, if capitalization is used correctly, write *C* on the lines provided. If a sentence needs revising, write your new version on the lines.

EXAMPLE

> In 1990, Learning Centres across Canada hosted numerous events celebrating International literacy year.
> In 1990, learning centres across Canada hosted numerous events celebrating International Literacy Year.

1. If you turn West on Northwest Walnut Street, you won't miss Central school.

   _____

2. The Committee member strode forward, shook the Chairperson's hand, and said, "Madam Chair, I support your new procedural proposal."

   _____

   _____

3. Some wealthy Business Executives resign their posts in order to seek new challenges in Business or Education.

   _____

   _____

4. Architects have commented favourably on designs for The Royal Bank Tower, which will eventually be built on the Northwest corner of Fifth street and Alder avenue.

_____

_____

_____

5. Nova Scotia's Grand Pré National historic park was established to commemorate the Expulsion of the town's acadian settlers between 1755 and 1763.

_____

_____

_____

ASSIGNMENT 40B IDENTIFYING AND CORRECTING CAPITALIZATION ERRORS

Often the most difficult part of proofreading is focusing on matters of correctness rather than content. Below you will find a frankly obnoxious letter posing as a job application. Do not pay attention to what this letter says. (This writer is confused about correct business letter style and format, among other things). Instead, focus on identifying and revising any capitalization errors. Read the letter, underline any word that uses capitalization incorrectly, and write your correction in the space between lines. The first such correction has been made for you.

N.E.
2000 n.e. main st.

ottawa, Ontario K1V 3M9

january 2, 1989

Acme Trading co.

43561 Shady lane

Kingston, ontario K7L 2M4

My dear Friends at Acme Trading,

Are You looking for a Self-starter—somOne who can Get the Job Done? I have had over Two Years of retail experience working for Waterbeds, Waterbeds, & waterbeds, Inc. During one Summer, I sold over six new complete packages. I sold waterbeds as Halitosis cures, Bunion relievers, and—o yes!—headache destroyers (so long as the head of the bed was facing West). I could sell a waterbed to the ghost of my Mother's grandmother. I could sell ice cubes on Sundays in Winter in the yukon. All of this convinces me that i AM

Management Material; your trainee program sounds perfect for me. Give Me the chance, and I'll get YOU the results you want.

Very Truly YOURS,

— 41 —

Using Abbreviations and Numbers

EXERCISE 41.1 USING ABBREVIATIONS FOR PERSONAL AND PROFESSIONAL TITLES

Proofread the following sentences for errors in the use of abbreviations. If the sentence is correct as written, write *C* after it. If the sentence needs revision, make your correction above the line.

EXAMPLES

general

The World War II invasion of Normandy was led by a Gen. who never went into politics: Omar Bradley.

Ms. Patricia Rozema's films have been selected to appear in many national and international film festivals. *C*

1. Some graduate students believe that a Ph.D. automatically leads to a good job.

2. The Rev. Eammon O'Conner led the singing, but Fr. McDill gave the sermon.

3. Thursday's presentation will feature Dr. JoAnne Trow, Ph.D.

4. Sir Thomas More, now recognized as a St., was an English statesman.

5. The profs. in the French Department decided to establish a composition prize.

EXERCISE 41.2 USING ABBREVIATIONS WITH NUMERALS

Read each sentence. If it uses unacceptable abbreviations, underline these abbreviations and write out the full versions on the lines provided. If the sentence as written is correct and acceptable in formal prose, write *C* on the lines.

EXAMPLE

The individual with the winning # will receive an annual income in excess of $60 000 + a contract to appear in lottery advertising. number, plus

1. We estimate that four workers will be required @ a rate of $21.00 per hour.

2. The airlines report one A.M. flight leaving on Tuesday.

3. Approximately seventy-two% of those polled agreed that religious beliefs were an important part of their lives.

4. The earthquake destroyed several downtown buildings, ruptured water & gas mains, and left hundreds homeless. _____

5. @ the current rate of interest, your total payment of principal + interest would = $792.25 per month. _____

6. Confucius lived at the time we would now identify as 500 B.C.

   _____

7. The $ that you requested has been approved by the grants committee.

   _____

8. The $450.00 that you requested has been approved by the grants committee.

   _____

9. Travelling at the km per hr you indicate, you would be in Montreal in an hour.

   _____

EXERCISE 41.3   USING ACRONYMS AND INITIAL ABBREVIATIONS

Identify five abbreviations or acronyms beyond those cited on pages 578 and 579 in the handbook. Give the abbreviation or acronym, spell it out, and use the abbreviation or acronym in a sentence. Then identify an audience that would recognize the abbreviation or acronym and identify another audience that might not recognize it. Use your own paper, and follow the format of the example.

EXAMPLE

> Abbreviation/Acronym: DWI
> Long form: driving while intoxicated
> Sample sentence: Jack was cited for his third DWI offense.
> Audience that will recognize this abbreviation/acronym: anyone in the criminal justice system
> Audience that might not recognize this abbreviation/acronym: anyone not familiar with law enforcement, drunk driving, or alcohol abuse

ASSIGNMENT 41A   AVOIDING THE MISUSE OR OVERUSE OF ABBREVIATIONS

Read the following sentences. Underline all abbreviations, and determine whether or not these abbreviations are appropriate for academic writing. If the abbreviations are appropriate, leave the sentences alone. If the abbreviations are inappropriate, write in the acceptable forms above the abbreviations. You may need to review earlier portions of this chapter.

EXAMPLE

for example
She recommended conservative investments—e.g., utility stocks and term deposits.

1. Blind Lemon Jefferson, Bessie Smith, Jelly Roll Morton et al. helped make the blues a popular style of music.

2. Vancouver is famous for rain, crocuses in Feb., the Canucks, and Stanley Pk.

3. On 5/18/81 Mt. St. Helens erupted with such force that it felled trees ten miles away.

4. After mother's death that Tues. in Aug., the family's dynamics changed considerably.

5. The last chapter of C. Brontë's *Jane Eyre* opens with this famous announcement: "Reader, I married him."

6. The S. Korean city of Kwangchu boasts a pop. of over 700 000.

7. The MacKenzie R. winds its way through the N.W.T., from Great Slave Lk. to the Beaufort Sea.

8. After weeks and months of planning, yrs. of scientific progress, and centuries of dreaming, on July 20, '69, a member of the human species walked on the moon.

9. The province of Alta. covers over 660 000 sq. km land.

10. Despite his knee injury, he still participates in low-impact activities like swimming, bicycling, walking, etc.

ASSIGNMENT 41B WRITING NUMBERS

Read the passage below for any errors in the presentation of numbers. Underline any errors you find, and make your corrections in the space above the line.

John Ruskin, an influential nineteenth-century British writer, was born in eighteen nineteen. Allowed few toys or friends, he had a lonely childhood, and learned to amuse himself with imaginative games and with study. He published an early essay at the age of 15; before his death in nineteen hundred, he would publish 100s of essays and lectures on a wide range of topics from art to travel to natural history.

On April tenth, 1848, at 4 o'clock in the afternoon, Ruskin was married to Euphemia Gray in Perth, Scotland. He was 29 and she was 19. Ruskin had met Effie when she was still a child, but developed stronger feelings for her during a visit she paid to his family just 2 years before they were married. His feelings for her were not, however, of a physical nature: for the next 7 years, until Effie divorced him, the marriage remained unconsummated. 1 year after the divorce, Effie married John Everett Millais, 1 of the young artists of the Pre-Raphaelite Brotherhood, a friend and former travelling companion of the Ruskins. This marriage was different in at least one respect: Effie went on to have 8 children—4 boys and 4 girls.

— 42 —

Using Italics

EXERCISE 42.1   USING ITALICS FOR FOREIGN WORDS OR PHRASES

Choose and circle five of the words or phrases from the list below. On your own paper, use each in a sentence. If the word or phrase should be italicized as foreign, be sure it is underlined in your sentence. You may need to consult a good dictionary for this exercise.

habeas corpus   sans souci

idée fixe   ex post facto

a priori   bon mot

gemütlichkeit   glasnost

habitué   bona fide

EXERCISE 42.2   ITALICIZING THE NAMES OF VEHICLES

Read the following sentences. Underline each name that should be italicized.

EXAMPLE

The corvette H.M.C.S. Sackville is docked in Halifax as a memorial to those who served in the Battle of the Atlantic.

1. The Bluenose, the famed racing schooner, is depicted on the Canadian dime.
2. In 1937, the explosion of the Hindenburg effectively ended the use of airships for passenger service.
3. Small passenger planes, Cessnas cruise at about 175 mph.
4. Lindbergh's famous flight in the Spirit of St. Louis took him over thirty-three hours.
5. The first Mercury capsule, Freedom 7, carried astronaut Alan Shepard at speeds exceeding 5000 miles per hour.

EXERCISE 42.3   USING ITALICS SPARINGLY FOR EMPHASIS

Briefly analyze the emphasis created by the use of italics in the following sentences. Use your own paper for this exercise.

EXAMPLE

I heartily agree with you.
Analysis: Italicizing *I* suggests that although the speaker agrees, someone else disagrees; italicizing *I* implies and highlights a contrast.

1. Will you ask the Johnsons to bring hamburgers *and* a potato salad?
2. When the scores were shown, it was clear that the judges could not find *anything* wrong with her diving performance.
3. With perseverance and care, we will *defeat* AIDS.

Write a sentence that contains one word italicized for emphasis, and explain what the emphasis is.

EXAMPLE

The *evidence* seems to suggest that Arnold is the culprit here.
Analysis: The sentence implies that something other than the evidence, perhaps Arnold's character, suggests he is not the culprit.

Now write the same sentence, but this time italicize a different word. Explain the new emphasis.

EXAMPLE

The evidence *seems* to suggest that Arnold is the culprit here.
Analysis: This version implies that the speaker does not believe the evidence; it is not what it seems.

ASSIGNMENT 42A USING ITALICS FOR TITLES AND FOR WORDS, LETTERS, OR NUMBERS REFERRED TO AS SUCH

Most (but not all) of the following sentences contain titles or other words that should be italicized. Underline these words. If the sentence is correct as written, simply go on to the next sentence.

EXAMPLES

A virtual institution of Canadian television, <u>Front Page Challenge</u>, still attracts a loyal audience each week. The word <u>separate</u> is one that many people misspell.

1. TV Guide's cover story discussed some of the old westerns: Bonanza, Gunsmoke, The Lone Ranger, and others.
2. After the fire, we had to replace our copies of the concertos by Beethoven as well as those of the Messiah by Handel.
3. Michel Tremblay's play Les Belles Soeurs opened in 1968; today it's a classic of the Quebec theatre.
4. When Kate Chopin wrote The Awakening, she couldn't have realized how many women would respond to that book.
5. Many English-speaking students take French classes to improve their employment prospects.
6. I'm reading Margaret Atwood's Lady Oracle for my English 2120 class.
7. Children's Digest, Chatelaine, Seventeen, Maclean's, and National Geographic—all those magazines arrived in the mails when I was a kid, and I read them all.
8. Last year we saw one of the four original, handwritten, fifteenth-century copies of the Magna Charta on temporary display at the Huntington Library.
9. The golden M of a McDonald's restaurant is often a welcome sight to the weary traveller.
10. I decided to submit poems titled "Recognition" and "Tired" to Poetry magazine.
11. Due to its consistent popularity with concert goers, Beethoven's Symphony No. 5 frequently appears in the repertoires of major orchestras.
12. The Lawsons renewed their subscription to Saturday Night magazine.

— 43 —

Using Hyphens

EXERCISE 43.1   USING HYPHENS TO DIVIDE WORDS AT THE ENDS OF LINES

Many of the following sentences employ unacceptable hyphenation. Read each sentence, and underline any improperly hyphenated word; make your correction in the space above the line. On the line below the sentence, explain briefly what is wrong with the use of the hyphen. If the sentence is acceptable as written, write *C* on the line.
(Note: Treat proper nouns like all other nouns.)

EXAMPLE

                                     wouldn't
    Ellen called to let you know that she <u>would-</u>

    <u>n't</u> be able to meet with you until after 2 P.M.

    <u>Contractions should not be hyphenated.</u>

1.   This afternoon, the four of us enjoyed a sun-
      ny October day in the park.

    _____

2.   If between now and the end of the month no precipit-
      ation falls, this will be the driest October since 1895.

    _____

3.   While we have been enjoying this spate of unseasonab-
      le weather, other parts of the country have received snow.

    _____

4.   Weather forecasters are predicting heavy rains and hur-
      ricane-force winds for this afternoon.

    _____

5.   The very first books, those printed during the fif-
      teenth century, are known as *incunabula*.

    _____

6.   Some fish possess modified muscle tissue that is cap-
      able of generating 450 to 600 volts of electricity.

    _____

7. The widely acclaimed actress Gertrude Lawrence had a career that spanned more than two decades.

8. In recent years, novelist Janette Turner Hospital has solidly established herself as one of Canada's foremost writers.

9. The first set of ratings figures for the fall season shows NB-
C leading its two American network rivals.

10. Baseball trivia buffs will recall the 1987 St. Louis vs. Min-
nesota World Series as the first in which the home team won every game.

EXERCISE 43.2   USING HYPHENS TO CLARIFY MEANING

Each of the questions below specifies a particular word. Use that word correctly in a sentence. Consult your dictionary if necessary.

EXAMPLE

pro-creation
The pro-creation camp has definite opinions about how science ought to be taught.

1. procreation
2. re-cover
3. recreation
4. re-creation
5. re-form
6. reform

ASSIGNMENT 43A   USING HYPHENS WITH COMPOUND WORDS AND COMPOUND MODIFIERS

Many (but not all) of the sentences below use hyphens or compound words incorrectly. Read each sentence. If hyphens and compounds are used correctly, write *C* on the lines provided. If the sentence needs revising, write your version on the lines.

EXAMPLES

Michael spent his afternoon entertaining the six-year-olds, seven-year-olds, and eight-year-olds.
Michael spent his afternoon entertaining the six-, seven-, and eight-year-olds.
Stained-glass artistry made the church distinctive and inspiring.
C

1. This is a brilliantly-argued position paper. _____

2. An Edmonton youngster was hospitalized yesterday after consuming a still to be determined quantity of mothballs. _____

3. Short-term forecasts indicate that we should plan for a rainstorm Wednesday. _____

4. When you drop off your completed form, we will check to make sure that you have an up to date file. _____

5. Several drop offs of over sixty feet make the Eagle Creek Trail a potentially dangerous one. _____

6. My grandparents left the mother-country in 1908. _____

7. Listening to the rock group Rush, you would never think they were just a three man band. _____

8. Many argue that abortion is not just a two-sided or three-sided question. _____

9. After two days of pitching and yawing on a fishing boat, I feel weak-kneed, windburned, and weather beaten. _____

10. He decided his I don't care attitude was too easy; besides, it left him feeling empty. _____

ASSIGNMENT 43B USING HYPHENS WITH PREFIXES AND SUFFIXES AND WITH FRACTIONS AND COMPOUND NUMBERS

Each item below is either a number or a word with a prefix or a suffix. Construct sentences that use the specified words correctly. Consult your dictionary as needed.

EXAMPLE

thirty-six + odd
After thirty-six-odd years, she trusted her own judgement.

1. half + back _____

   _____

2. self + control _____

   _____

3. trans + continental _____

   _____

4. quasi + professional _____

   _____

5. machine + like _____

   _____

6. mid + stream _____

   _____

7. anti + freeze _____

   _____

8. pre + adolescent _____

   _____

9. post + Trudeau _____

   _____

10. un + important _____

    _____

11. 2/3 (write using words) _____

    _____

12. 405 222 (write using words) _____

    _____

13. 4000 (write using words) _____

    _____

14. president + elect _____

    _____

15. pre + high school _____

    _____

ASSIGNMENT 43C USING CORRECT HYPHENATION

Proofread the sentences that follow for incorrect end-of-line hyphenation or other inaccurate hyphenation. Underline the errors you find, and correct each in the space above it. Consult a dictionary whenever necessary. If the sentence is acceptable as written, write *C* after it.

EXAMPLES

When I get up late and have early morning appointments, I may <u>care-</u>
lessly skip breakfast.　　　*carelessly*
<u>I have never learned how to find B sharp.</u> *C*

1. We spent over a week in class discussing the various pro-

    cedures relating to soil testing.

2. The lakefront was dotted with log cabins and A frames.

3. I was driving home from work when I saw a young de-

    er bound across a field by the highway.

4. B flat and C-major are both musical notes.

5. With candy, cookies, cakes, nuts, and cider, our Halloween fes-

    tivities were definitely high in calories.

6. They decided that the U pick farm had the biggest, ripest strawberries they had ever seen.

Answers to Preview Questions

Compare your answers to Part Preview Questions with those provided here. If you were unable to answer a question, or if your answer conflicts, find the first bracketed chapter reference following the answer given below. That chapter will be one that you should study closely.

PART 4 1) Meryl, car, supermarket 2) McCraes pet, doctor 3) will get, finishes 4) might speak, going 5) Anybody, those who, his 6) Which, you 7) Until, under, up [Chapter 13] 8) I 9) whom 10) Whom 11) he, she 12) me [Chapter 14] 13) am 14) doesn't 15) gave 16) lay 17) would 18) wants [Chapter 15] 19) its 20) a 21) travels 22) have 23) is [Chapter 16] 24) well 25) most 26) really 27) nicer, nicest [Chapter 17]

PART 5 1a) no 1b) no 1c) no 1d) yes [Chapter 18] 2a) yes 2b) no 2c) yes 2d) yes [Chapter 19] 3a) yes 3b) no 3c) no 3d) yes [Chapter 20] 4a) no 4b) yes [Chapter 21] 5a) yes 5b) no 5c) no [Chapter 22] 6a) no 6b) yes 6c) yes 6d) yes [Chapter 23]

PART 6 1a) yes 1b) no [Chapter 24] 2a) so 2b) but 3) no 4a) When the rain started 4b) who gave me this watch 4c) even though she left an hour early [Chapter 25] 5a) no 5b) yes 5c) no [Chapter 26] 6a) wordiness 6b) C 6c) passive verbs, wordiness 6d) weak verb 6e) passive verb [Chapters 27 and 28]

PART 7 1) X ("tons" is informal language) 2) sentence acceptable 3) X ("he's just wrong" is too extreme; readers who disagree may feel offended) [Chapter 29] 4) eludes (alludes) 5) stink (fragrance, aroma, or scent would be better) 6) continuously (continually), continual (continuous) 7) C [Chapter 30] 8a) for instance: biology, biography, biochemistry 8b) for instance: juror, jurisdiction, jurisprudence, justice, justify 9) -ly 10) -ive, -ic, -able, -ful, -ish [Chapter 31] 11) Latin, *adjudicatus*, past part. of *adjudicare*, to judge 12) premature dementia, schizophrenia 13) trend, drift, current, inclination, tenor 14) six-ten [Chapter 32] 15) Their (They're) 16) definately (definitely), desert (dessert) 17) herd (heard), developped (developed) 18) rein (reign), righters (writers), dyed (died) 19) nucular (nuclear), treatey (treaty) [Chapter 33]

PART 8 1) ... shared much, they ... 2) ... cousin, lives ... 3) ... china was totally ... [Chapter 34] 4) ... at first; however ... 5) ... positions: short-order ... 6) ... a "book-house," I ... [Chapter 35] 7) ... Marisa asked. 8) P.K. Page ... 9) ... one's writing?" they ... 10) ... shouted "Stop!" [Chapter 36] 11) ... judges' ... defence's ... 12) ... just doesn't want ... 13) ... eight o'clock ... 14) C 15) ... was theirs. [Chapter 37] 16) "I did not know ... evening," Peter said. 17) ... was 'very taxing,'" Vincent ... 18) ... windy," the ... 19) ... robbers "are now in custody." 20) ... novel *Robinson Crusoe*. [Chapter 38] 21) ... literature: good ... 22) C [Chapter 39]

PART 9 1) capitalize *We*; do not capitalize *northwestern* 2) do not capitalize *they* 3) C 4) C 5) capitalize *Renaissance* and *Middle Ages* [Chapter 40] 6) "a doctor" and "an M.D." say the same thing; use one or the other when referring to a single person or group 7) C 8) AD (A.D.) 9) #

(number) 10) Nfld., Ont. (Newfoundland, Ontario) 11) 6 (Six) 12) 10,000 (ten thousand) [Chapter 41] 13) *Hebrew Bible*, *Gospels*, *Koran* (none of these should be italicized) 14) "King Lear," "Shakespearean Negotiations" (italicize; do not use quotation marks) 15) C 16) C 17) "in medias res" (italicize; do not use quotation marks) 18) C 19) "Annie Hall" (italicize; do not use quotation marks) [Chapter 42] 20) best-known (do not hyphenate) 21) C 22) cloud-less (do not hyphenate), rain- ed (do not divide) 23) C 24) better-coverage (do not hyphenate) 25) C 26) man- uscripts (do not begin a new line with a vowel) [Chapter 43]

Answers to Chapters

— 13 —
Constructing Grammatical Sentences

Exercise 13.1 Identifying Verbs

Notice that <u>not</u> is an adverb and is not part of the verb phrase. Here are the verbs or verb phrases that should <u>be</u> underscored.

1. reads   2. will be finished   3. must tell   4. has, been washed   5. make   6. will, choose   7. lifts

Exercise 13.2 Identifying Nouns

Here are the nouns that should be underlined:

1. hour, Leonard, wood
2. Marcia, glasses
3. Angie, Harry, hours, highway
4. quiche, The Valley
5. dog, hair, winter
6. *Sports Illustrated*, article, Mike Tyson
7. mother's, cookies

Exercise 13.3 Identifying Pronouns

Here are the pronouns that should be underlined:

2. Our
3. that, his
4. Most, us
5. Her, her
6. Everyone, who
7. That, we, its

Exercise 13.4 Identifying Adjectives

Here are some samples of adjective-noun pairs.

1. <u>old</u> calendar   2. <u>paperback</u> book   3. <u>squeaky</u> shoes   4. <u>useless</u> key   5. <u>broken</u> laces
6. <u>polished</u> silver

Exercise 13.5 Identifying Adverbs

Sample sentences are given below. Yours may differ; if in doubt about a sentence, ask your instructor.

149

2. The cleaners will <u>finally</u> be finished with your coat on Friday.
3. Alice, you <u>really</u> must tell me before tomorrow.
4. That mug on his desk <u>definitely</u> has not been washed in three weeks!
5. Grosbeaks make a <u>truly</u> distinctive sound.
6. I will <u>almost</u> always choose broccoli over asparagus.
7. Music <u>always</u> lifts my spirits.

Exercise 13.6   Identifying Prepositional Phrases

Here are the prepositional phrases that should be underlined.

2. in the hotel lobby after work
3. After a meal, of turkey, potatoes, creamed onions, for dessert
4. With the exception, of my chemistry class
5. With so many blouses, in stock
6. for your Panasonic printer, in the latest shipment
7. for the poetry prize, before April 1

Exercise 13.7   Identifying Conjunctions and Interjections

Here are the conjunctions that should be underlined once:

2. Before   3. either, or   5. and, and, and, and, and   6. so that   7. so

Here is the interjection that should be underlined twice.

4. Ouch!

Exercise 13.8   Identifying Subjects and Predicates

1. His <u>coffee</u> <u>tasted</u> too strong.
2. The phonograph <u>needle</u> <u>skips</u> every time.
3. That <u>telephone</u> <u>has rung</u> constantly all morning.
4. April <u>rains</u> <u>have refilled</u> the reservoirs.
5. The fishing <u>season</u> <u>opens</u> soon.
6. The typewriter <u>ribbon</u> <u>was fixed</u> last night.
7. Her <u>letter</u> <u>answers</u> every question.

Exercise 13.9   Identifying and Using Direct and Indirect Objects

Here are the direct objects that should be underlined once:

3. speech   4. sound   6. copy   7. principal

Here are the indirect objects that should be underlined twice:

4. listeners   6. Mrs. Zanefeld

Sample sentences are given below:

8. a. Uncle John gave my brother a present.
   b. Uncle John gave a present to my brother.
9. a. Ricky threw me the football.
   b. Ricky threw the football to me.
10. a. Officer Malone handed Susan the ticket.
    b. Officer Malone handed the ticket to Susan.

Exercise 13.10   Using Prepositional Phrases

Sample sentences are provided below. Check with your instructor if you are unsure of your answers.

1. Before lunch, Sanjay felt ill. (phrase functions as an adverb)

2. Her speech on abortion convinced me. (phrase functions as an adjective)

3. The barn in Johnson's field is a local landmark. (phrase functions as an adjective)

4. The plumbers will repair that leak in the morning. (phrase functions as an adverb)

5. After the phone call, Carole announced she was leaving. (phrase functions as an adverb)

Exercise 13.11   Using Infinitives, Gerunds, and Participles

Correct answers should contain the specified verbal, but the rest of the phrase may differ from the sample answers given below.

1. running 2. Hurrying to my seat 3. to sprint faster 4. To lose weight 5. To improve at the cello, to practise regularly 6. vacationing in the mountains 7. Battered by the storm

Exercise 13.12   Identifying Dependent Clauses

Here are the dependent clauses that should have been underlined:

that the surf looked a little high
After we were seated in the kayak and headed into the waves
Before we had time to think
When we struggled to shore half an hour later
who had been watching
what he said
though for a while there I wasn't sure that you would

Exercise 13.13   Understanding Function and Form

1. Either you take me to the store, or I'll run away!
   Function: exclamatory; Form: compound

2. Although we received considerable precipitation during April, the drought is not over.
   Function: declarative; Form: complex
3. Is it true that Lake Park Roller Rink has been closed? Function: interrogative; Form: complex
4. While we were sleeping, Alec went to the store for us , and he has even fixed us dinner!
   Function: exclamatory; Form: compound-complex
5. I can still taste the delicious Cajun chicken that you prepared for us last night. Function:
   declarative; Form: complex

Assignment 13A   Identifying the Parts of Speech

1. car: noun; sped: verb; barely: adverb; pedestrians: noun
2. you: pronoun; should have read: verb; before: preposition; class: noun
3. As: conjunction; winds: verb; it: pronoun; and: conjunction; becomes: verb
4. Yes: interjection; ten: adjective; snow: noun; on: preposition
5. That: pronoun; essay: adjective; question: noun

Assignment 13B   Using Linking Verbs and Subject Complements

Samples are given below.
1. From the deck, the lights looked quite beautiful.
2. That sweater you're wearing today is particularly stylish.
3. On Saturday the ocean was turbulent.
4. That perfume is delightful.
5. That painting looks incredibly realistic.
6. This car is a Buick LeMans.
7. That track star is Wilma Rudolph.
8. A piano is a particularly versatile instrument.
9. Those buildings are dentists' offices.
10. The two celebrities were Madonna and Sean Penn.

Assignment 13C   Understanding Linking, Transitive, and Intransitive Verbs

Sample answers are given below.

1. Beth handed Tina a note.
2. The dog brought us the stick.
3. Charlie passed his mother the butter.
4. Sally threw Agnes the scarf.
5. Music gave the audience peace.

You should have identified the underlined verbs as follows:

6. linking
7. transitive
8. transitive
9. intransitive
10. linking

Assignment 13D   Using Phrases

Sample answers are provided below.

1. Monica called Harold after work.
2. Feeling ill, Harold called to cancel their date.
3. Named after bodies of water, Nippers Harbour, L'Anse au Loup, and Little Burnt Bay can all be found in Newfoundland.
4. Also provincial court judge, Thomas Chandler Haliburton established himself as an important 19th-century Canadian writer.
5. Swimming every other morning keeps Lisa fit, and she enjoys it.
6. To lose weight safely, you should watch your diet and exercise regularly.
7. Before washing the baby, test the water.
8. Lighting the sky, the warehouse burned fiercely.
9. Colin James, a rock and blues singer gaining a national reputation, will appear in concert next week.
10. Ears ringing and hands aching, I left the concert and headed for my car.

Exercise 13E   Using Clauses

Sample sentences are provided below. If you are unsure of your answers, check with your instructor.

1. (dependent clause) You should seek other advice before you decide.
2. (independent clause) Bruce caught the ball on the run, but he was tackled before he could score.
3. (independent clause) By the time I checked the bowl, the candy had disappeared.
4. (dependent clause) The class that you suggested was already full.
5. (dependent clause) When Horowitz appeared, the cameras rolled, and the Russian audience applauded.
6. (independent clause) A gentle wind stirred the yard, and elm leaves swayed overhead.
7. (independent clause) When we saw it, the abandoned car was covered with rust.
8. (dependent clause) After we'd finished dinner, I cleared the table, and I insisted that mom sit down.
9. (independent clause) The paper was nowhere to be found, so I went to the store for a new copy.
10. (independent clause) After she found what she was looking for, she closed the file drawer.

Answers will vary. Sample answers are given below.

11. Interrogative sentence: Did she find what she was looking for?
12. Interrogative sentence: When we saw it, wasn't the abandoned car covered with rust?
13. Imperative sentence: You sit down while I clear the table.
14. Imperative sentence: Seek other advice before you decide.
15. Exclamatory sentence: I can't believe the class you suggested was already full!
16. Exclamatory sentence: Horowitz appeared, the cameras rolled, and the Russian audience went wild!

— 14 —

Understanding Pronoun Case

Exercise 14.1   Using Subjective Case Pronouns

1. Whenever they visited the beach, the weather was bad.
2. As the cattle crossed the road, they stopped all traffic.
3. Chris was a better tennis player than he.
4. The rhododendrons are most beautiful in May when they bloom.
5. We were the only people still in the building.
6. Tom wondered if he was smarter than James.
7. Allison was curious to see whether or not she would be asked to work late.
8. Symphonies are popular, but not all cities have them.
9. The cars slowed to a stop whenever they approached an on-ramp.
10. Dick, Brad, and I have a great time whenever we get together.

Exercise 14.2   Using Pronouns to Distinguish between Gerunds and Participles

1a. This sentence carries the same meaning as *We clearly saw their signalling*. Whose signalling? their signalling. (gerund)
 b. This sentence indicates that the signalling itself was clear. Signalling how? signalling clearly. (participle)
2a. This sentence implies that the singing itself was bad. How did they sing? without regard for our comfort. (participle)
 b. This sentence implies that the singing was quite good. The sentence could be reordered this way: Without regard for our comfort, we heard their singing. Presumably only superior singing would compel an uncomfortable audience to listen. (gerund)
3a. This sentence implies fear on the part of the watchers. How did we watch? cautiously. Like the others above, this sentence could be reordered: Cautiously we watched his tightrope walking. (gerund)
 b. This sentence indicates how he was walking: cautiously. (participle)

Exercise 14.3   Using *Who* and *Whom* to Begin Questions

1. Whom   2. Who   3. Who   4. Whom   5. Who

Exercise 14.4   Using *Who, Whom, Whoever,* and *Whomever* to Begin Dependent Clauses

1. ... showed up to listen; she showed up to listen; subject: whoever
2. ... she trusted; him she trusted *or* she trusted him; object: whom
3. ... he instructed to write this brief; her he instructed to write this brief *or* he instructed her to...; object: whomever
4. ... enjoys skiing on fresh powder; she enjoys skiing on fresh powder; subject: who

154

Assignment 14A   Using Objective Case Pronouns

1. With a long week behind us, a brisk Saturday walk gives Sonja and I some much needed exercise.
2. When Pam finished dinner, Julie reminded her to study physics.
3. Charlie asked her to give him a call later.
4. Eventually the headwaiter told Kim, Sidney, and me that we could be seated.
5. After three days of steady rain, gale force winds toppled several trees and left them looking like huge, spilled matchsticks.
6. For Bill, Monty, and me, running 25 kilometres a day was our training for the marathon.
7. Before we could say anything more, Amy loaned Oscar and me thirty dollars.
8. C
9. Tony called her before he left the house.

Assignment 14B   Using Subjective, Objective, and Possessive Case Pronouns

1. His; us   2. Their; them   3. her   4. He; himself; he   5. she; she; his; her; her; him

Assignment 14C   Using *Who, Whom, Whoever,* and *Whomever*

1. whom functions as the object of the preposition *to*
2. Whoever functions as the subject of the verb *informed*
3. Whom functions as the object of the verb *should notify*
4. whom functions as the object of the verb *describe*
5. whom functions as the object of the verb *called*; whoever functions as the subject of the verb *is.*
6. Who functions as the subject of the verb *called*
7. who functions as the subject of the verb *phoned*
8. who functions as the subject of the verb *do vote*

Assignment 14D   Using Correct Pronoun Case with Appositives

1. City life is what we Torontonians thrive on.
2. For us Nova Scotians, history is everywhere.
3. For two Newfoundlanders, her and Bernie, the flatness of Saskatchewan came as quite a shock.
4. As newcomers Dale and I found out, Sudbury has a long history of mining.
5. Lute Johannson always claimed he was the best of us chili cookers.
6. There is only one whisky to us real Scots.
7. Two Irish natives, she and William Butler Yeats, must share the title of best writer.
8. The committee gave the two finest storytellers, Ed and me, citations of merit.
9. That country house looked good to us longtime apartment dwellers.
10. Even to Les and him, the computer eventually proved to be a powerful tool.

—— 15 ——

Using Verbs

Exercise 15.1 Using Auxiliary Verbs

1. I is running for the position of class president. [should be I am running]
2. After careful study, we inclined to accept the consultant's report. [should be we are inclined or we were inclined]
3. Whenever Veronica misses school, you can bet she has developed another ear infection. C
4. Since Ravi has been reading Robert Louis Stevenson, he don't watch much television. [should be he doesn't watch]
5. When the alarm bell rings, we must leave the building immediately. C

Exercise 15.2 Distinguishing between *Lie/Lay*, *Sit/Set*, and *Rise/Raise*

2. sit 3. lain 4. set 5. sat 6. lay 7. laid 8. lie 9. lay [takes transitive form with direct object *myself*.] 10. sat, set 11. raised 12. rises

Exercise 15.3 Using Verb Tenses in Sequences

Note that in sentences that need rewriting, there may be more than one acceptable way to accomplish such revision. Only one example is provided in each case below.

1. had designed/past perfect/designs/simple present Liz Claiborne designed dresses before she designed eyewear and other accessories.
2. was/simple past/proved/simple past   L
3. will have left/future perfect/arrive/simple present   L
4. had changed/past perfect/crumples/simple present
   The light had just changed to green when the pickup truck crumpled the passenger side of my Volkswagen.
5. had started/past perfect/will go/simple future
   The soap opera had just started when our power went out.

Exercise 15.4 Identifying Active and Passive Voice

1. analyses (active)
2. are analysed (passive)
3. pounded (active)
4. was eaten (passive)
5. will be fishing (active)
6. says (active)
7. was put (passive)
8. put (active)

9. had been returned (passive)
10. contributed (active)

Exercise 15.5   Identifying Verb Moods

Here are the verb moods.

meet (indicative)
were (subjunctive)
needs (indicative)
ask (imperative)
moved (indicative)
thought (indicative)
speaks (indicative)
are (indicative)
Keep (imperative)
were planning (subjunctive)

Exercise 15.6   Using Verb Moods

Answers will vary. Sample sentences are given.

1. Please carry this kindling downstairs.
2. This court summons insists that Philip appear tomorrow.
3. Sometimes Brenna wished that she were more involved in local politics.
4. Monkeys climb trees with enviable agility.
5. Call me tomorrow about that order.

Assignment 15A   Using Verb Forms

Answers will vary. Here are sample sentences.

1. I walked home after school.
   When you saw me, I was walking home after school.
2. They ask that you change the due date for their paper.
   They had asked for food before.
3. The neighbours' birds screeched all night.
   Yes, the neighbours' birds are screeching again!
4. When we vote, we decide who should represent us.
   We had decided on those vacation dates before we learned of your plans.
5. Those teenagers consumed three dozen hamburgers and two cases of pop.
   When I left the picnic, the teenagers were consuming the last of the carrot cake.

Assignment 15B   Using Irregular Verbs

Answers will vary. Here are sample sentences.

1. When we were young, we thought that adults could do whatever they wished.

2. They brought fresh salmon to the potluck.
3. Over the years, Paul has become a close friend.
4. The circus has begun.
5. I had forgotten/forgot that experience until now. [or any appropriate auxiliary used with *forgotten*/*forgot*]
6. We drew pictures of bowls of fruit.
7. During their long match, the contestants both drank water often.
8. They had felt that tired only once before.
9. The ice cubes were frozen in an hour. [or any appropriate auxiliary with *frozen*.]
10. I was passed by a Mack truck. [or any appropriate auxiliary with *passed*.]

Assignment 15C   Using the Present Tenses

Answers will vary. Sample sentences are given.

1. He is quickly climbing the corporate ladder.
2. Old Uncle Max has been marrying younger women since 1962.
3. McPhee's essays often discuss matters of geology and natural history.
4. With this awards ceremony, we are beginning a new tradition.
5. People have teased John about his bald spot for years now.
6. A hungry dog devours its meal.
7. I have been confusing the twins' names for years.
8. According to his driver's licence, he is lying about his age.
9. Sue has sat in that chair all day.

Exercise 15D   Using the Past Tenses

Answers will vary. Here are sample sentences.

1. Sheila rode her horse for an hour before beginning her homework.
2. When we found the baby, she had drunk only a little bit of the mouth-wash.
3. Mary had stolen his heart, but then he met Lisa.
4. Sandy had been walking for two hours before he realized he was lost.
5. That year we were protesting the bombing of Cambodia.
6. In those days, regulations required visitors to leave the dorms by ten o'clock.
7. We had been enjoying the picnic until the rain started.
8. She was driving down The Alameda when I first saw her.
9. I had only slept for two hours when you woke me.
10. The elephant's floppy ears delighted Ari.

Assignment 15E   Using the Future Tenses

Answers will vary. Here are sample sentences.

1. This time next year, I shall be deciding what to put in my resumé.
2. Andy will remember that picnic once you begin talking about it.
3. By the night of the awards ceremony, Loreen will have composed her acceptance speech.

4. When the shuttle lands next Friday afternoon, the astronauts will have been flying for a little over six days.
5. All next week the Sisleys will be fishing for tuna off the Prince Edward Island coast.
6. Next Saturday, the exchange students will have been visiting for two months.
7. Before the committee reaches its decision, it will have consulted a variety of experts.
8. I will oppose any attempt to amend this proposal.
9. Laurie will have hiked twelve kilometres by sunset.
10. Next summer, we will be celebrating the completion of this project.

Assignment 15F Using Verb Tenses in Logical Sequence

Note that for some of the sentences below, either the main verb *or* the dependent clause verb can be changed in order to create a logical sequence. Thus, for each sentence that needs to be rewritten, there may be more than one correct revision. Only one of the possible revisions is given.

1. I had just finished spading the garden when you came out with the cold drinks.
2. On the first sunny Saturday in April, we decided to take a hike.
3. L
4. Before we started to eat dinner, we emptied the dishwasher.
5. The committee needs to meet for an extra hour next week.
6. L
7. They will announce the winners after we finish dessert.
8. Mark had just stepped out of the shower when the lights started to flicker.
9. Anita had surgery last month and hopes to begin training again next week.
10. Some Canadian historians would love to have lived in 1867.

Maintaining Agreement

Exercise 16.1   Maintaining Subject-Verb Agreement

(Saguenay Park), situated near Chicoutimi, Quebec, *consists* consist of nearly 300 square kilometres of land on both sides of the Saguenay River. (One) of the park's most striking features *is* are the Saguenay fjord. Created during the Ice Age by glaciers that gouged through the Laurentians to the St. Lawrence River, the (fjord) today *makes* make a dramatic sight for nature-lovers. (Visitors) sometimes *spot* spots whales, which are native to the fjord. (Naturalists) at the park's Visitor Centre *describe* describes the park's wildlife in more detail and *explain* explains how the fjord was formed. In addition to the fjord, there *are* is many (paths) for hikers. The (trails) wind through the forested valley, which hugs either side of the river. (One) of the trails *leads* lead to the top of cap Trinité. At the summit, a (statue) of the Virgin Mary stands 183 metres above the river. Such dramatic (sights) *make* makes Saguenay Park well worth a visit.

Exercise 16.2   Making Verbs Agree with Relative-Pronoun Subjects

The correct verb forms are:

1. are   2. arrive   3. like   4. affect   5. enter

Review Exercise 16.3   Checking Subject-Verb Agreement

Here are the verbs and their correct forms.

appreciate (appreciates)
is
keeps (keep)
do know
is (are)
bothered
makes
are (is)
irritating
is (are)
disgusted
smells (smell)

sees (see)
enjoy
taste (tastes)

Exercise 16.4 Maintaining Accurate Agreement

A sample paragraph has been provided below.

My ideal dinner begins with a plate of fresh vegetables: baby carrots that were picked that morning, washed radishes with their tops still on, sliced green pepper, and half a dozen thin rounds of cucumber. After this vegetable plate comes a small crab cocktail that is made with Dungeness crab legs and a tomato and Tabasco sauce. Some Alpine White Riesling would taste delicious with the crab. For a main dish, I would specify fresh Atlantic salmon that has been grilled and lightly spiced. Accompanying the salmon would be several choice broccoli florets that have been steamed until tender, as well as a couple of new potatoes boiled in their skins. After such a sumptuous repast, dessert could only be a modest bowl of truly expensive vanilla ice cream accompanied by black coffee.

Listing of subjects and their verbs, pronouns and their antecedents:

Sentence 1
dinner/begins, that (referring to carrots)/were picked
their/radishes
Sentence 2
cocktail/comes, that/is made
that/cocktail
Sentence 3
Alpine White Riesling/would taste
Sentence 4
I/would specify, that/has been grilled and spiced
that/salmon
Sentence 5
florets/would be accompanying, that/have been steamed
that/florets their/potatoes
Sentence 6
dessert/could be

Exercise 16A Maintaining Agreement with Compound Subjects

1. subjects: witnesses, officers; verb: was
   Rewrite: Neither the witnesses nor the police officers were able to identify the hit-and-run driver positively.
2. subjects: witnesses, officer; verb: were
   Rewrite: Neither the police officer nor the witnesses were able to identify the hit-and-run driver positively. [Preferred version]
   or: Neither the witnesses nor the police officer was able to identify the hit-and-run driver positively.
3. subjects: car, occupants; verb: were
   C

4. subjects: you, driver; verb: were
   Rewrite: Either you or the other driver was responsible for the accident.
5. subjects: company, you; verb: is
   Rewrite: Either the insurance company or you are going to pay for repairs.

Sample answers are given.

6. Barbara and Chris live on a pleasant suburban street not far from Garfield School.
7. Papers and midterms challenge students every term.
8. After several weeks of classes, each paper and midterm becomes a challenge.
9. My sister and confidante visits us next week.

Assignment 16B Maintaining Verb Agreement with Collective-Noun or Indefinite-Pronoun Subjects

1. Subject is: group (a collective noun); verb is: go
   Rewrite: The group that white-water canoes the Nahanni River goes home deeply affected by the experience.
2. Subject is: Neither (indefinite pronoun); verb is: are
   Rewrite: Neither of these auditioners is right for the part.
3. Subject is: Most (indefinite pronoun); verb is: use
   C
4. Subject is: band (collective noun); verb is: play
   Rewrite: That band [as one unit] plays a spirited rendition of "God Save the Queen."
5. Subject is: Some (indefinite pronoun); verb is: is
   C

Assignment 16C Reviewing Subject-Verb Agreement

1. The hands of the clock say 3:15.
2. C
3. Whenever it rains, I wear a coat.
4. C
5. The telephone operator who told me the arrival times was unnecessarily rude.
6. Among the best dishes in that restaurant is grilled lamb. [normal word order has been reversed; subject is lamb]
7. One of their great hopes in the last several years has been a trip to Scotland.
8. The glaucous gull and the western gull are often found inland during the stormy winter months.
9. Rum and Coke combine to make a popular alcoholic drink.
10. Pie and ice cream has always been our favourite dessert. [one unit, one dessert]
11. C
12. Tom and Liz, who also happen to be married to each other, each wear glasses.
13. Neither a graphic artist nor three proofreaders have been able to improve this poster.
14. C
15. C
16. C
17. Good news often goes unreported.
18. Anybody taller than six feet knows it can be difficult to find clothes that fit.
19. It is mathematics that causes me the most trouble in university.
20. C

Assignment 16D   Making Pronouns Agree with Compound or Collective-Noun Antecedents

Here are the pronouns, their antecedents, and correct sentences.

1. its/deer and bobcat
    Deer and bobcat populations stabilized once their habitats were preserved.
2. their/each
    By August, each gardener and homeowner is proud of his or her crop of squash.
3. his/Luc or Marie
    When we drive home tonight, either Luc will have to take the projector home in his car or Marie will have to take it home in hers.
4. him/brothers
    Nobody saw them, but the Anderson brothers washed Mrs. Wright's car.
5. it/Bravo Company
    Bravo Company has decided that they will take separate cars to camp and meet by the mess hall at noon.
6. its/committee
    C
7. their/Jenny or she
    Jenny or she called her parents with the good news.

Assignment 16E   Making Pronouns Agree with Indefinite Pronouns and Avoiding Sexist Usage

1. C
2. Replace "his" with "their."
3. C
4. Replace "her" with "him or her."
5. Replace "his or her" with "their."
6. Replace "his" with "his or her."
    or rewrite:
    Those who have finished the course should receive their certificates in two weeks.
7. Replace "their" with "his or her" (twice)
    or rewrite:
    In 1980, residents of Quebec had to make their own decisions about the future of their province.

— 17 —

Using Adjectives and Adverbs

Exercise 17.1   Writing with Adjectives and Adverbs

A sample paragraph is provided below, with the five adjectives and adverbs and the words they modify listed afterwards.

   Some misguided people think of cycling as an exercise to be performed fiercely and joylessly while astride the narrow seat of a racing bike, speeding along some impossibly long and arduous route. Not me. With my bicycle's wide, padded saddle and its eighteen gears, and with my city's endless stretches of beautiful bike trails, cycling is for me the perfect way to enjoy sunny summer days while exercising my heart and lower body—mildly. When cycling beside the sparkling river, should a person pedal so furiously that the gorgeous view is reduced to a blur? When winding along a wooded path, should a cyclist tear along so determinedly that mosquito-plastered sunglasses are the only memory of the tranquil forest? I think not. When summer arrives majestically, in all its fresh, quiet splendour, when my bicycle is freed from winter storage, I cycle to drink in the beauty of nature, not to pass it by.

Five adjectives: *misguided*, modifying people
　　　　　　　　narrow, modifying seat
　　　　　　　　long, modifying route
　　　　　　　　padded, modifying saddle
　　　　　　　　sparkling, modifying river
Five adverbs:　　*fiercely*, modifying to be performed
　　　　　　　　impossibly, modifying long and arduous
　　　　　　　　mildly, modifying exercising
　　　　　　　　furiously, modifying should pedal
　　　　　　　　majestically, modifying arrives

Exercise 17.2   Using *Good, Well, Bad, Badly, Real,* and *Really*

Here are the correct adjectives or adverbs.

1. good 2. really 3. good 4. well 5. badly 6. really 7. real 8. bad

Exercise 17.3   Using Comparative and Superlative Forms

1. I. Replace *larger* with *largest*.
2. I. Replace *slowest* with *slower*.
3. C
4. I. Replace *fancier* with *fanciest*.
5. I. Replace *more* with *most*.

164

Assignment 17A   Identifying and Correcting Adjective-Adverb Errors

Here are the adjective-adverb errors and their correct forms.

clear (clearly)
cloudlessly (cloudless)
occasional (occasionally)
rare (rarely)
sluggish (sluggishly)
weary (wearily)
stupid (stupidly)
tiredly (tired)
real (really)
fierce (fiercely)
happy (happily)
really (real)

Assignment 17B   Using Comparative and Superlative Forms

Sample sentences are given below.

1. Candice seems more serious this year than she did last year.
2. Of the four passengers in the car, the most seriously injured was a teenager who suffered a broken arm.
3. For me, algebra is more confusing than geometry.
4. This is the worst June weather we have had in five years.
5. Of the three auditioning violinists, the second one played best.
6. After another cold night in her snowcave, Marie felt worse.
7. Most audiophiles prefer listening to compact disc recordings.
8. I'm hungrier now than I was an hour ago.
9. Lennie's dive will be more difficult than Ron's.
10. When you have written well, it feels like the most rewarding activity in the world.

—— 18 ——

Maintaining Clear Pronoun Reference

Exercise 18.1   Identifying and Revising Confusing Pronoun Usage

Note that there will often be more than one correct way to revise these out-of-context sentences. Only one possibility is provided in each case below. If you are unsure of your revisions, consult your instructor.

1. During the student union election campaign, the Rahey-Utgoff debates forced Rahey to articulate his positions.
2. The council, the mayor, and the city controller agree that the mayor must change her management style.
3. Jack liked Yvette and was still technically going steady with Sheila; finally, he decided to ask Sheila to the prom.
4. C
5. The marriage counsellor or was not sure how her first session would go with Barbara and Donald.

Exercise 18.2   Using *Who, Which, That, You*, and *They*

There may be some minor variations in how your sentences are revised. Use the revisions below as a guideline.

1. We had planned on watching *Masterpiece Theater* on Sunday evening, but since the television station had transmission problems, we watched the CBC movie instead.
2. C
3. Customers who shop carefully for a used car can often make a satisfactory deal.
4. The Wrights expected a large crowd on Halloween night, and sure enough, the trick-or-treaters came to their door one after another.
5. Typing classes often bore the students who take them, but afterwards those students are glad they can type.
6. A dog that has been specially trained can give a blind person new mobility.
7. Whenever a customer walks into that stereo store, the salespersons approach immediately rather than letting the customer browse.

Assignment 18A   Identifying and Revising Vague, Ambiguous, or Wordy Pronoun Usage

Your changes may differ somewhat from those listed below. Any revision that eliminates pronoun usage problems is acceptable. Sample answers are listed.

that (who)
which (who/that)
they (these students)
they (these classes)

166

you (students)
It is a class that (This class)
they (students)
they're (these students are)
It is important that ... his (School board members should consider their)

Again, your changes may be different from those listed below. If in doubt about your revisions, consult your instructor.

they (Darlene and Chris)
them (the second one) (the instructions)
it (about the project)
them (the components)

Assignment 18B   Maintaining Clear Pronoun Reference

In many cases, more than one accurate revision is possible. Compare your answers with the samples below.

1. C
2. The picture that you drew and that I hung on the wall has provoked many favourable comments.
3. The picture that you drew and that I hung on the wall has provoked many favourable comments, even though the wall itself is peeling in places.
4. She plans to drive her Rover, which has given her trouble in the past, over Santiam Pass.
   or
   She plans to drive her Rover over Santiam Pass, a route that has given her trouble in the past.
5. The plumbing company placed an order with Lee Tool & Die, but Lee Tool & Die was sold before they could fill that order.
6. We painted over the offensive graffiti on the fence that bordered our parking lot.
7. The committee discussed one proposal to raise taxes and another proposal to freeze them; eventually they passed the tax increase proposal.
8. C
9. After fifteen weeks, negotiators reached a settlement that included two holidays and new provisions for vacation time.
10. Witnesses said the car that hit me barrelled around the corner and swerved to my left.

Recognizing Shifts

Exercise 19.1 Identifying and Revising Confusing Shifts in Tense

The incorrect sentences may be accurately revised in more than one way. Only one sample answer is given for each sentence.

1. Ann measured the flour and poured it into the bowl.
2. We paint the inside wall Friday, work in the garden on Saturday, and go to the beach on Sunday.
3. C
4. The winds, which were blowing at almost gale force, capsized the rubber raft just as it reached the mouth of the river.
5. C

Here are all the verbs that should be underlined (revisions are shown in parentheses):

occurs (occurred), left, resulted, will wander (wandered), settled, Said, holds, know, like, to lie, can, [It's], said, indicate (indicated), was swerving (swerved), to miss.

Exercise 19.2 Identifying and Revising Confusing Shifts in Person and Number

There may be more than one correct way to revise these sentences; only one version is indicated for each of the sentences below.

1. If one visits the local art museum, one will find on display paintings by Mary Pratt.
2. Sea anemones thrive in coastal tidepools, but they cannot survive outside the water for very long.
3. When an amateur photographer takes pictures, he or she often enjoys the activity as much as the finished prints.
4. C
5. Weekend runners are prime candidates for running-related injuries, especially if they get no exercise during the week.
6. Tourists should be aware that road crews are busy on Highway 34, and drivers should.expect some delay at the Oglesby Bridge construction site.
7. Whenever newspaper carriers go on vacation, they should make sure they have arranged for substitutes to take over their routes in their absence.

Exercise 19.3 Avoiding Shifts Between Direct and Indirect Discourse

This exercise calls for four discussion sentences, each based on a different source. Two of these discussion sentences should be direct discourse (quotations) and two should be indirect discourse (paraphrase). Compare your discussion sentences with the examples included in the exercise.

Exercise 19.4 Avoiding Shifts in Tone and Diction

While there may be room for reasonable disagreement here, the revisions indicated below seem preferable.

Listen folks, these guys and gals are only out to empty your wallet! (These business people are motivated only by greed)
make no bones about (do not conceal)
that's you, bucko! (meaning you)
the moola up front (payment in advance)
sit on your manuscript (delay all work on your manuscript)
turkeys (inferior)

Review Exercise 19.5 Recognizing and Revising Inappropriate, Unnecessary, or Confusing Shifts

Suggested revisions are shown in parentheses following each shift in the original prose.

some bozo (a customer),
If one is (If you are)
if one believes (if you believe)
one (you)
You ain't there to raise folks' fashion consciousness; you're there to provide courteous service (You are employed to provide courteous service regardless of customers' tastes)
could not come (cannot come)
he or she should have called the store manager (call the store manager)
they told anyone (telling anyone)
felt frustrated (feel frustrated)
were obligated (are obligated)
some big spender (a valued customer)
make sure you said (say)
welcomed (welcomes)
or say, "we will gladly set this merchandise aside for you." (or say that you will gladly set the merchandise aside for the customer)
returned (return)
made (make)

Assignment 19A Identifying and Revising Confusing or Unnecessary Shifts in Mood and Voice

1. verbs: asked, report, presents
   Rewrite: The chair asked that Milena report the subcommittee's findings and present its recommendations.
2. verbs: were gathered, arranged
   Rewrite: Lionel gathered and arranged the roses.
3. verbs: requires, pass, defends
   Rewrite: The graduate school requires that a master's student pass exams and defend his or her thesis.
4. verbs: leave, water, should lock
   Rewrite: Before you leave tonight, water the plants and lock the doors.

5. verbs: delivered, were delivered
   Rewrite: The construction company delivered lumber Monday afternoon, and the wiring and plumbing materials later in the week.
6. verbs: Say, should say
   Rewrite: Say no to their request, but say it tactfully.
7. verbs: congested, delayed
   C
8. verbs: asks, fill (out), returns
   Rewrite: The credit company asks that an applicant fill out an application and return it within fourteen days.
9. verbs: suggests, brings, arrive
   Rewrite: The invitation suggests that Tanya bring roller skates and arrive at two o'clock.
10. verbs: were to become, was elected, would celebrate
    Rewrite: If Suzanne were to become president and if Kelly were elected treasurer, then we would celebrate with a dinner out.

—— 20 ——
Identifying Comma Splices and Fused Sentences

Exercise 20.1   Identifying and Revising Comma Splices and Fused Sentences by Separating Independent Clauses or by Linking Them with a Semicolon

While you may disagree about the best revision choice, you should be able to see that the sentences in questions 1 and 4 are somewhat more independent of each other than the sentences in questions 2 and 3. By this reasoning, questions 1 and 4 have been revised as separate sentences. Questions 2 and 3 have been revised with semicolons.

1. F. Begin new sentence at "forsaking."
2. CS. Substitute a semicolon for the comma after "taste."
3. F. Insert a semicolon after "shows."
4. CS. Replace comma after "towns" with a period. Begin new sentence with "Added."
5. C.

Exercise 20.2   Linking Independent Clauses with Commas and Co-ordinating Conjunctions

Again, there may be some disagreement regarding the choice of co-ordinating conjunction. Sample sentences follow.

1. The crocuses and daffodils bloomed early, as April turned out to be unseasonably warm.
2. Jack's employee evaluation was mostly positive, but he was laid off due to a shortage of orders.
3. Claire was reading Ray Smith's *Lord Nelson Tavern*, and she thought it a very strange book.
4. Maybe we should plan on discussing this tomorrow at the staff meeting, or maybe we should call a special meeting that would include the other working group.
5. Alice was concerned that her chemistry books were overdue, but the due date stamped in the back told her she still had two days to return them.

Exercise 20.3   Linking Independent Clauses with Semicolons and Conjunctive Adverbs or Transitional Phrases

Any logical conjunctive adverb or transitional phrase taken from the lists in the text is acceptable. Sample sentences are provided here.

1. The sign urged that those of you who partake of alcoholic beverages refrain from the operation of your automobiles; in other words, if you drink, don't drive.
2. No rains fell in Saskatchewan for over six weeks; consequently, grain farmers suffered significant losses.
3. With all the travelling we do, we couldn't possibly own a dog; besides, the apartment rules forbid pets.
4. One month she can't talk or even sit up by herself; then she's standing wobbly-legged against the furniture and calling, "Ma, Ma."

5. The hostile reviews of his novel *Jude the Obscure* caused Thomas Hardy considerable pain and distress; indeed, the criticism contributed to his decision to give up writing fiction.

Assignment 20A Revising Comma Splices and Fused Sentences

There can be little dispute about the underlined sentences; the revision choices, on the other hand, are many. A sample revision is supplied below.

Perhaps the most striking fact about people is that they make things. When early October arrives, swallows migrate dogs get heavier coats snakes go into a kind of hibernation people knit themselves caps. People without caps and people with too many caps get together and invent the set of promises we call money. Having invented money, people pay other people to make parkas and slickers or they use money to buy kits and make these things themselves. Rain pelts down deer seek the densest cover they can find people build houses with roofs. When cats get cold, they curl into tight little balls.People invent insulation or they pay sheep ranchers to provide the wool that's made into warm shirts. When caribou get hungry, they have no choice but to seek a new range. When people get hungry they don't move eventually they invent pizza.They figure out how to cure olives they figure out how to make thick bread crusts, they experiment with anchovies and pineapple they invent beer. Indeed, people are makers.

Perhaps the most striking fact about people is that they make things. When early October arrives, swallows migrate, dogs get heavier coats, and snakes go into a kind of hibernation. People, however, knit themselves caps. People without caps and people with too many caps get together and invent the set of promises we call money. Having invented money, people pay other people to make parkas and slickers, or they use money to buy kits and make these things themselves. When rain pelts down, deer seek the densest cover they can find; people, on the other hand, build houses with roofs. When cats get cold, they curl into tight little balls. People invent insulation, or they pay sheep ranchers to provide the wool that's made into warm shirts. When caribou get hungry, they have no choice but to seek a new range. When people get hungry, they don't move; eventually, they invent pizza. They figure out how to cure olives and how to make thick bread crusts. They experiment with anchovies and pineapple. They invent beer. Indeed, people are makers.

Assignment 20B Distinguishing between Co-ordinating Conjunctions and Conjunctive Adverbs or Transitional Phrases

Various combinations and revisions are possible. Samples are given below.

1. The birds were singing, and the sunlight shone through the slats of the bedroom's venetian blinds.
2. She awoke feeling unusually optimistic; in fact, she felt like she might sing out loud.
3. My diet plan says I can eat four ounces of fish for dinner, or I could choose the same amount of chicken.
4. Deer are curious animals; consequently, they will often run a short distance, stop, and look back.
5. The sun rises early on a June morning; however, the chorus of robins and bluebirds and sparrows starts even earlier.
6. For a long time, childhood had seemed distant, forgotten; however, that morning, standing at the window and hearing geese, she remembered a little girl held by her father, both of them looking up.

7. Salal grows in dense, green bushes, but when it blooms, the dainty blossoms are no larger than your smallest fingernail.

8. The lumber industry provides jobs for many workers in British Columbia as well as for some other provinces; even so, some Canadian jobs are lost when the logs are exported.

9. Rattan furniture is constructed when the materials are wet and pliable, yet those same materials prove both tough and durable once they have dried.

10. The leading economic indicators all registered modest drops yesterday; hence the stock market dropped in today's trading.

11. The Academy Awards telecast is often criticized as boring and too long; however, it consistently garners high ratings.

Assignment 20C   Revising Comma Splices and Fused Sentences by Using Dependent Clauses or by Making Two Independent Clauses into One Independent Clause

For each, a sample sentence is given for a revision using a dependent and an independent clause, and then for a revision using one independent clause.

1. Since the School of Education receives applications from more individuals than it can admit, the school carefully screens all applications.
   Receiving applications from more individuals than it can admit, the School of Education screens all applications carefully.
2. After the committee discussed the zoning variance for thirty minutes, they approved it on a 5−3 vote.
   After discussing the zoning variance for thirty minutes, the committee approved it on a 5−3 vote.
3. The premier, who is a Liberal, has decided not to attend the national party convention this month.
   The premier, a Liberal, has decided not to attend the national party convention this month.
4. Although computer technology changes rapidly, few businesses can afford to take advantage of every new advance.
   Few businesses can afford to take advantage of every new advance in the rapidly changing field of computer technology.
5. Breakfast, which consisted of fresh strawberries, homemade biscuits, and scrambled eggs, was served promptly at 9 A.M.
   Served promptly at 9 A.M., breakfast consisted of fresh strawberries, homemade biscuits, and scrambled eggs.

— 21 —
Recognizing Sentence Fragments

Exercise 21.1 Identifying and Revising Phrase Fragments

Here are the underlined phrase fragments and sample revisions.

1. In just a few miles/Enclosed by electrified fences
   Rewrite: He was surprised at how the countryside changed. In just a few miles, the car dealerships and fast food restaurants were replaced by rolling pasture enclosed by electrified fences.
2. From family members, from her clergy, and from qualified social workers/With the father/Certainly an interested party/To her own conscience, then make her own decision
   Rewrite: When a woman is considering abortion, she ought to seek counselling from family members, from her clergy, and from qualified social workers. She ought to talk candidly and at length with the father, certainly an interested party. Above all, she ought to listen to her own conscience, then make her own decision.
3. Called *Singing in the Rain*/During the filming
   Rewrite: Dancing in the rain was something Gene Kelly did in a movie called *Singing in the Rain*. It probably wasn't actually raining during the filming. More likely, the movie crew rigged a rain machine over the set.
4. C
5. To extend the deadline for completion of your degree requirements/By August of this year
   Rewrite: The committee has spent the last several days carefully reviewing your proposal to extend the deadline for completion of your degree requirements. We are happy to be able to tell you that an extension has been granted. Your requirements must now be completed by August of this year.

Exercise 21.2 Identifying and Revising Compound-Predicate Fragments and Dependent-Clause Fragments

Here are the sentence fragments:

When the city council convenes a special hearing on the proposed Sylvan Green Development Project./And specifies widening McKean Boulevard to accommodate increased traffic. The developers, who have already invested over $300,000 in architectural fees and permits./Argue that all city zoning requirements have been met.

That nightly deliveries might cause considerable noise./When the hearing convenes tonight at 7:30 in council chambers.

Here is one possible revision.

Community residents will have their final say tonight when the city council convenes a special hearing on the proposed Sylvan Green Development Project. The project has already received preliminary approval from the council. The development proposal calls for the construction of two anchor stores in its first phase and specifies widening McKean Boulevard to accommodate increased

174

traffic. The developers have already invested over $300,000 in architectural fees and permits. They argue that all city zoning requirements have been met. Local residents and developers have clashed at two earlier meetings.

According to opposition leaders, residents worry that nightly deliveries might cause considerable noise. And those opposed have also voiced concern over increased traffic at the school crosswalk at Oak and Fifty-sixth. When the hearing convenes tonight at 7:30 in council chambers, those opposed to the development promise fireworks.

Exercise 21.3 Identifying and Revising Sentence Fragments

Here are the sentence fragments:

About them as people./And do nothing but worry./When the test day arrives and they aren't prepared./As motivation to make study plans./In addition to reviewing notes and doing some selective rereading./And then construct appropriate answers./And probably don't spend much time in preparation./The most naturally gifted in this group./May still do reasonably well on tests./If they don't study.

Here is one possible revision:

How people take tests says something about them as people. Some individuals worry. And do nothing but worry. They don't reread, they don't review their notes, and they don't discuss major issues with classmates. After all this, they may still be surprised when the test day arrives and they aren't prepared. Other people worry, but they put that worry to work. These individuals use their worry as motivation to make study plans. In addition to reviewing notes and doing some selective rereading, these students might also try to anticipate test questions and then construct appropriate answers. In effect, they take practise tests. Then there are the people who don't worry at all. They don't take tests seriously and probably don't spend much time in preparation. The most naturally gifted in this group may still do reasonably well on tests. However even the most naturally gifted may be cheating themselves if they don't study. As my grandma used to say, "If you've never worked hard, how do you know how hard you can work?"

One fragment has been retained: *And do nothing but worry*. This fragment has been retained because its appearance here emphasizes the degree of worry.

— 22 —
Recognizing Misplaced, Disruptive, and Dangling Modifiers

Exercise 22.1   Identifying and Revising Misplaced Modifiers

Note that there may be more than one reasonable placement for the misplaced modifiers below; see especially answers 3 and 5. Only one example has been given for each sentence.

1. "Barking" should go directly before "dog."
2. "Almost" should go directly before "$2,000."
3. "Only" should go directly before "at 9:15 A.M."
4. "Even" should go directly before "the meteorologist."
5. "Indoors" should go directly before "if."
6. "inadvertently" should go directly before "said."
7. "Nearly" should go directly before "warm."

Exercise 22.2   Identifying and Revising Squinting Modifiers

1. (Employees entering this area) routinely (are required to wear safety gear.)

2. (The defendant promised) during the trial (he would obey the judge's instructions.)

3. (Margie felt) often (Jack was considerate and good with the children.)

4. (The renters promised) faithfully (to honour the conditions of the lease.)

5. C

1. Employees routinely entering this area are required to wear safety gear. Employees entering this area are routinely required to wear safety gear.
2. During the trial, the defendant promised he would obey the judge's instructions. The defendant promised he would obey the judge's instructions during the trial.
3. Margie often felt Gerard was considerate and good with the children. Margie felt Gerard was often considerate and good with the children.
4. The tenants faithfully promised to honour the conditions of the lease. The tenants promised to faithfully honour the conditions of the lease.
5. C

Exercise 22.3   Identifying and Revising Dangling Modifiers

Here are the phrase and clause modifiers that should be underlined.

When stricken by spring fever/Consulting authorities/Enduring hard winters/Happy at the return of good weather and hoping for good luck/Dotting the skies over Calgary/Though pleased by the avalanche of orders

Here is one revised version:

When stricken by spring fever, people sometimes suffer disastrous results. Although not fatal, this disease can lead to loss of productivity. Authorities agree that the specific symptoms include lassitude, a lack of motivation, an eagerness to spend long hours prone under sunlight, and an unwillingness to concentrate. Spring fever is a particular problem for those who endure long winters. Once May arrives, Torontonians have been known to leave their offices as early as 1 P.M. on Friday afternoons. Happy at the return of good weather and hoping for good luck, some Maritime shop owners post "Gone Fishing" signs. People admire hot air balloons dotting the skies over Calgary. Actually, spring fever means trouble only to the manufacturers of small wading pools for children. Though pleased by the avalanche of orders, companies must keep their factory buildings humming night and day to meet the demand.

Assignment 22A   Identifying and Revising Disruptive and Dangling Modifiers

Here are the disruptive modifiers that should be underlined. Sample revisions are also given.

1. although more expensive and sometimes hard to locate
   Although more expensive and sometimes hard to locate, fresh fish tastes better than fish that has been frozen.
2. After years playing chess
   After years playing chess, Jackie found the game got boring.
3. after a particularly bad week both at work and at home
   After a particularly bad week both at work and at home, Dierdre decided to visit her sister for the weekend.
4. Looking both ways
   Looking both ways, the children decided the traffic was too heavy to cross the street safely.
5. Eating his lunch
   Eating his lunch, he could hear his stomach begin to growl.
6. in the *Music Man*, which opened last night
   In this morning's newspapers, John Davidson got rave reviews for last night's opening performance of the *Music Man*.
7. C
8. Happy and no longer tired
   Happy and no longer tired, she saw the finish line appear at last at the bottom of the hill.
9. Before jogging regularly
   Before jogging regularly, one should purchase a good pair of running shoes.
10. following a dinner of roast beef, peas, and mashed potatoes
    The candidate gave a speech supporting the Prime Minister's foreign policies, following a dinner of roast beef, peas, and mashed potatoes.

— 23 —
Maintaining Consistent and Complete Grammatical Structures

Exercise 23.1 Matching Subjects and Predicates

This is a relatively difficult exercise. The first sentence, for example, requires major overhaul and rewording rather than the substitution or repositioning of a word or two.

The reason people can recognize a smooth collie is because they look like collies but when they're full grown their hair is short.[1] Smooth collies are where they have the same general build as their hairier cousins (called rough collies) and the same long noses.[2] But probably their most important characteristic is where like other collies they have great dispositions.[3] The nature of collies will accept abuse that would snarl or even bite.[4] Small children can sit on collies or hold their paws as if shaking hands.[5] Collies will even tolerate someone playing with their food.[6] Actually, collies are so lovable to hurt or tease them.[7] They're loyal, and they're so excited to see you in the morning that their brown eyes make you glad you got out of bed.[8] Collies are also superior intelligence.[9]

Here is one possible revision:

Smooth collies are easily recognizable; only their short hair makes them different from the more common long-haired (or rough) version. Smooth collies have the same general build as roughs and the same long noses. Both breeds possess great dispositions. A collie's good nature allows it to accept abuse that would make other dogs snarl or even bite. Small children can sit on collies or hold their paws as if shaking hands. Collies will even tolerate someone playing with their food. Actually, collies are so lovable that no one would want to hurt or tease them. They have superior intelligence, they're loyal, and they're so excited to see you in the morning that their brown eyes make you glad you got out of bed.

Exercise 23.2 Using Elliptical Structures Carefully

1. Kamal gets along well with Cecilia, and he gets along well with Don, but he does not get along well with Bev.
2. We could clearly hear Radio Moscow yesterday, but the signal is faint today.
3. During the summer, Ben plays softball on Tuesdays, tennis on Wednesdays, and soccer on Thursdays.
4. Harold decided to take a nap, Michael decided to study for his chemistry test, and Susan decided to take a book back to the library.
5. The car's exterior is blue, but the seats are black vinyl.

Assignment 23A Recognizing and Revising Garbled Prose

Here is a list of troublesome sentence parts and omissions:

literally their

of paper
that having to retype the entire document
italic or boldface type
changes the number of characters can be printed on one line
and no excuse for failing to revise

Here is one possible revision:

Writers familiar with word processing programs have a variety of skills literally at their fingertips. Such writers can move paragraphs or sentences from one part of a paper to another. They can revise sentences or whole passages without having to retype the entire document. They can experiment with the sizes of the margins and with italic or boldface type. Some printers are even equipped with adjustable pitch, a feature that allows changes in the number of characters that can be printed on one line. In short, word processing programs make revisions easy and give writers no excuse for failing to revise. For all of these reasons, writers who use computers are often considered more productive by employers.

Assignment 23B Identifying and Revising Confusing Sentences

Sample answers are given for each sentence.

1. The newspaper said that instead of beginning at 8:30, the sale would start at 9:30.
2. On average, 50% more rain falls here than falls east of the mountains.
3. Before we reorganized the books, they were stacked on those shelves that reached as high as the ceiling.
4. C
5. Not only was the tape dispenser empty, but the light bulb had burned out.
6. Most electric coffeepots come equipped with a thermostat that shuts off the electricity when the pot boils dry.
7. To find the financial aid office, go to the third floor of the administration building.

Assignment 23C Checking for Inadvertent Omissions and for Incomplete Comparisons

Here are possible responses.

1. Her play in today's match was better than her play yesterday.
2. If we can believe the newspaper, the weather yesterday was the same in Victoria as it was in St. John's.
3. The firewood was stacked neatly in the wooden rack by the back door.
4. This piano is in better tune than the piano at home.
5. Entitled *Dance on the Earth*, Margaret Laurence's memoir chronicles the life and times of this admired Canadian author.
6. The Rambo movies appeal to a different audience than does the movie *Bambi*.
7. These days, summer boredom seems worse for twelve-year-olds than it does for young children or for teenagers.
8. C
9. C
10. Although it is generally high in sodium and fat content, fast food tastes better than salad when you are very hungry.

— 24 —
Constructing Effective Sentences

Exercise 24.1   Revising Wordy Prose

Here is one possible revision:

   If I think back to my childhood growing up in the city, I can remember Toronto's street cars. Their parallel tracks crisscrossed downtown streets, and their over-head wires mirrored the tracks. The cars were big and sturdy and shook the streets with their rumbling. Inside, they were run down, with red paint peeling and seats oozing their cotton stuffing. Perhaps because the cars themselves were in sorry shape, it always seemed that the riders were in similar condition. Some of them were drunk, some just rambled to themselves, and some just needed showers. For a four-year-old, riding in a street car produced an interesting mixture of fear and excitement. The fear was of those other passengers: Would they simply continue dozing peacefully? Would they stand up raving? Would they hurt children? The excitement came from experiencing something unfamiliar and unpredictable.

Assignment 24A   Using Climactic Order

Here are a few possible revisions.

1. Coast Guard personnel conduct boating safety classes, routinely monitor emergency radio channels, and must sometimes risk their lives to save others.
2. After a distinguished career as a diplomat and after serving as a member of the federal Cabinet, Lester B. Pearson became Prime Minister.
3. Jamaica produces citrus fruits, bananas, allspice, and its most important crop, sugarcane.
4. Martin Luther King helped establish the Southern Christian Leadership Conference in 1957 and became its first president that same year, but most agree that his career as a civil rights leader reached its high point in August 1963 when he addressed over 200,000 protesters at the Washington Monument.

Assignment 24B   Being Concise

Sample answers are given.

1. Today, welfare reform remains an important issue.
2. Many experts believe that workers on graveyard shifts make more errors than day workers.
3. Von asked me to turn in his paper for him if he did not return to campus by 9 A.M.
4. The sandwich you made tasted fresh and delicious.
5. We agree that the paper originally due on Monday will now be due on the following Friday.

—— 25 ——
Creating Co-ordinate and Subordinate Structures

Exercise 25.1 Using Co-ordination and Subordination for Special Effect

Two examples of repeated co-ordination:

She travels all over the world, and meets interesting people, and makes a sizeable salary, and has swarms of men around her, and she still thinks her life is boring!

I've read a book, and I've cleaned my apartment, and I've gone grocery shopping, and I've jogged three miles, and it's not even 11:00 A.M. yet.

Two examples of repeated subordination:

If you like rich desserts, if you crave chocolate, if you die for sweets, then you'll love the cake that John baked.

When it starts to rain, when your clothes are soaked, when your mascara runs down your face, then it's time to buy a new umbrella.

This is an example of repeated co-ordination/subordination:

"And Piper Gunn went home and hung up his bagpipes and they have been silent from that day to this, for he died soon after, and no one ever dared play them, for no one could ever play the pipes like Piper Gunn himself could play them."
Writer: Margaret Laurence
Book or publication you found it in: *The Diviners*. 1974.
Toronto: Seal-McClelland and Stewart-Bantam, 1975.

Assignment 25A Using Co-ordination

Sample sentences are given.

1. Sharon wanted higher grades on her written work, so she studied to improve her spelling.
2. During the storm, we heard tree trunks snap, and we saw the weird, blue light of electrical transformers as they shorted out.
3. The sun did not come out today, for the rain never stopped.
4. Karen thought she would have trouble with the math class, but she earned an A on the last test.
5. Saturday we will have spaghetti for dinner, or we may have beef stroganoff.

Assignment 25B Using Subordination

There will be more than one correct answer for these sentences. Here are some samples:

1. The computer disk that you gave me was the wrong size.

181

2. When making career decisions, students should think about what makes them happy as well as about what will make them wealthy.
3. Although he was sick with a cold last week, Reggie turned in his paper on time.
4. Until a dog bit their daughter, Emily and John were looking for a pet.
5. Greg's works, which included both paintings and drawings, were featured for three weeks at the Guistina Gallery.

— 26 —
Creating and Maintaining Parallel Structures

Exercise 26.1   Using Parallel Structures in Revision

Here is one possible version; revised material has been underlined.

When faced with the task of moving from one town to another, we decided to save money by tackling the entire job ourselves.[1] We quickly discovered that moving was not fun—it was hard work.[2] The physical work was tiring enough, but, the decision making was even more difficult.[3] Should we sell Aunt Maude's needlepoint pillow with the moth hole, or should we pack it lovingly in a box?[4] Occasionally we agreed on such things, but, more often, we disagreed.[5] Then we either continued packing in a tense silence, or we told jokes to defuse the situation.[6]

Through trial and error, we discovered that the heaviest items should go into the smallest containers.[7] Thus, books went into the smallest boxes, small lamps (minus the shades) and shoes went into the midsize boxes,[8] and the lightest goods—such as clothing, bedding, and towels—went into the largest boxes.[9] We also learned that not only must all boxes be carefully packed, they must also be carefully stacked.[10] Small, heavy boxes crush those which are large and airy.[11] But neither careful packing nor careful stacking could tell us exactly what was inside an unlabelled box.[12]

Exercise 26.2   Analysing Parallel Structures and Their Effects

1. a) These are parallel. The parallelism highlights the contrasts. Giving the parents the last word suggests that the writer agrees with the parents.
   b) These are not parallel. The wordiness of the second sentence weakens its effectiveness.
   c) These are parallel. The either/or construction makes for a balanced, impartial statement. It is difficult to tell who this writer agrees with.
2. a) These are parallel sentences, however their short length makes them seem choppy and child-like. Either the writer here is childlike or Joe is.
   b) These are parallel structures. Combining the sentences in this way makes for a more sophisticated, adult impression. Without the short sentence "Joe wants a lot of things," readers get only a list. Adding that short sentence may begin to imply that this writer thinks Joe is greedy.
   c) These are not parallel sentences. The wordiness and informality creates an impression of someone speaking. The last sentence here is particularly awkward.

Assignment 26A   Using Parallel Structures

There are a number of ways to revise these sentences so that they are parallel. Some samples are given below.

1. Pierre preferred to do his own landscaping, his own roofing, and his own carpet installation.
2. parallel words: designs; manufactures; provides; (structures parallel)
3. On a clear day, you can see west to the Bay of Fundy, east to Minasville, and north to Parrsboro.
4. The firefighters asked that spectators remain calm and stay a safe distance away.

183

5. This week, Parliament may vote on child care legislation, or it may postpone action until after the holiday recess.
6. Comprehensive health insurance, job security, and the right to strike—those were the union's main demands.
7. The road wound down out of heavily forested mountains, through pasture land, and into the city.
8. She ate cold pizza for breakfast, and she ate lobster for dinner.
9. parallel phrases: by candidate A with his fiery rhetoric; by candidate B with his impossible promises
   (structures parallel)
10. Some of World War I's bloodiest fighting occurred at the Somme River, and some of World War II's bloodiest fighting occurred on the beaches at Normandy.

— 27 —
Varying Sentence Structures

Exercise 27.1   Identifying Various Sentence Openings

As we ate (3)
After such a brilliant sunset (2)
Unfortunately (1)
Disappointed only a little bit (2)
Because we were clumsy and maybe still a little sleepy (3)
As you can imagine (3)

Exercise 27.2   Revising Prose by Varying Sentence Lengths and Sentence Openings

Here is one possible revision:

Though we do not often pay attention to them, land use issues are important. But when a developer decides to change the character of our neighbourhood, then land use becomes a personal issue. Then we pay attention. We know about this because the field behind our house has been slated for clearing, grading, and construction. What has been a place for forts and games for our children will soon become a new shopping centre. That means cars and noise, but it could also mean new shops and a better local selection of goods. It might even mean a fancy new restaurant or two. So sometimes we think the development is a good idea, benefiting the community and providing jobs. But sometimes we don't want that field to change. Trying to understand this particular land use issue, the whole family goes to planning commission hearings. We listen to the developer; we listen to our neighbours. For us, land use isn't some foggy, distant issue anymore. It's as close as our backyard.

Exercise 27.3   Adding Sentence Variety

Here is a sample freewrite:

I am in school for an education and to make friends—need to decide what my career goals are, and I think more education can help me with that. Also I want to study subjects I would never be able to learn about on my own. And I'm meeting new people from different backgrounds and with different ideas about the world. What else? I'm learning how to be independent or maybe that's not something you learn, but it just comes with experience. A good education is important today. It opens doors for you and lets you make choices. You can do anything you want. I know it takes a lot of work, but it will be worth the effort. University forces me to make decisions about how I spend my time, what to study, which people I like, and which groups—if any—I want to join. It also changes your attitudes because you are in an environment with people who come to this place with new ideas. The most important thing you learn in university is how to make decisions.

Here is a reasonably representative revision of the earlier freewrite:

University provides me with unique opportunities (1). Not only am I receiving valuable academic training in my major, I am also learning the tricky business of decision-making (2). Should I take the 9:00 course with Berg or the 11:30 course with Dale? (7) Should I take the required course this term, or should I take the elective that I know will not be offered again until next year? (7) Not only do I choose my courses and subjects, but I also choose my friends and my extra-curricular activities (2). Do I want to spend all afternoon playing ultimate frisbee? (7) Do I want to spend *every* afternoon playing ultimate frisbee? (7) Suddenly I find that I am choosing from a wider range of possibilities than I've ever had before (3).

University provides unique challenges (1). It forces us to make life decisions, to deal with rigid time boundaries, to taste independence, perhaps for the first time (6). I know that the choices I am making now will pay off in the future, for making choices is a lifelong activity (4).

Assignment 27A   Writing Sentences of Varying Lengths

There will be many possible revisions for these sentences. Compare your answers with these examples.

1. Watch out for that truck!
2. Begin by stripping the original finish. Complete any rough sanding. Use fine steel wool to smooth the table's exposed surfaces. Finally, apply the new finish.
3. People who have trouble with math often say they study and study, take the test, and then find themselves disappointed with the results.
4. Despite frustration and weariness, despite self-doubt and the ridicule or indifference of others, hard work eventually achieves its goal.
5. A good, thick clam chowder with French bread and maybe a glass of Riesling makes for a delicious Friday lunch.

Creating Memorable Prose

Assignment 28A Revising by Choosing Stronger Verbs

Here are sample revisions.

1. The murder mystery on television bored me so much that I fell asleep.
2. Many parents waited in the parking lot to pick up their children.
3. In many cities, burglars threaten neighbourhood security.
4. Most political cartoonists argue that a candidate's looks are more important than a candidate's positions on the issues.
5. In Munich, excited Canadian fans watched figure skater Kurt Browning capture his third consecutive world championship.
6. The personal lives of actors and actresses fascinate many of their fans.
7. Many computer programs require at least 256 kilobytes of memory.

Assignment 28B Choosing between the Active and the Passive Voice

1. passive/Intended emphasis: my sister Kate
   My sister Kate won an honours medal.
2. passive/Intended emphasis: dogs and cats
   OK
3. passive/Intended emphasis: the Province of Ontario
   The Province of Ontario hereby summons you to appear in Small Claims Court on July 21 at 10 A.M.
4. passive/Intended emphasis: we
   In summer, we often see soaring red tail hawks high over the meadows.
5. active/Intended emphasis: the aftershocks
   In the next eight minutes, five aftershocks were recorded by seismographers.

Assignment 28C Composing Sentences That Use Special Effects

Of course, many sentences are acceptable for this exercise. Below are some sample sentences for you to compare with yours. If you are unsure of any of your sentences, check with your instructor.

1. Repetition: I paid for the drinks and I paid for the dinner; I paid for the movie and I paid for the popcorn; I paid for the taxi home, and I even paid the tip, and then my friend asked me to lend him ten dollars.
2. Antithesis: We went to Barbados seeking a suntan; we came back from Barbados seeking skin cream.
3. Inversion: Out of the airplane and into his arms walked his long-lost sister.

Assignment 28D   Styling Sentences

Sample revisions follow.

1. As I got off the bus, I looked in my backpack for my keys. When I couldn't find them there, I tried my pocket—still no luck. Although I distinctly remembered locking the door after me that morning, I could not figure out where those keys were now. The sight of the totally dark apartment gave me a sinking feeling as I walked to the door. Even as I rang the bell, I knew the truth: my roommates were not home, and I was locked out.

2. Today's shoppers lack the time for careful price comparisons. As a result, they tend to accept higher prices. Of course, merchants take advantage of this willingness to spend more. Thus retail prices remain high, a situation which actually discourages comparison shopping. The net effect of all of this is simple: these days, there is no such thing as a bargain.

Establishing Tone

Exercise 29.1 Varying Tone to Fit Your Audience

Here is a sample letter to the manager:

222 Selham Place
Halifax, N.S.
B1S 3G2
Sept. 8, 1990

Joe House, Manager
A Place to Eat
777 Melbourne St.
Halifax, N.S.
B2P 4A2

Dear Mr. House,

Last night I had dinner at your restaurant. At the urging of Frank, my waiter, I ordered the Chef's Special. When the entree arrived, I noticed an odd odour, but said nothing. The chicken possessed an unusual texture, and the cheese sauce (which I scraped off) was distinctly bitter, perhaps mouldy. However, since I did not wish to cause a commotion during what was otherwise a quite enjoyable evening with friends, I ate what I could of this meal.

About twenty minutes after leaving your restaurant, I began to feel ill. In truth, nausea and other unpleasant symptoms kept me up most of the night. I have no wish to involve a lawyer in this matter, as I have had several quite good meals at A Place to Eat. Nevertheless, I do ask for a refund for the cost of this meal, $23.40 including tax. Please send a cheque to the above address, and we shall consider this unpleasant matter closed.

Sincerely

Nancy Green

To a friend:

Dear Helen,

You won't believe the meal I had two nights ago. Several of us went to A Place to Eat—you know, it's new, on the other side of Robie, about a block from Lena's place. Anyway I went with the special since Frank the waiter said it was good. Good, he said! It was mouldy chicken in an ancient cheese sauce. Of course, not wanting to spoil the evening, I went ahead and ate about half of it. The real fun began when I got home. We're talking big-time illness here. I still feel like I went ten rounds with somebody punching me in the stomach. Last time we darken their door. We need to get together soon. How about lunch this week? Someplace downtown, ok? I'll call you. Love and kisses,

Nancy

Exercise 29.2 Increasing Your Awareness of Appropriate and Inappropriate Language

Here is a sample of a final draft:

When I think of offensive language, I think of ignorant people using terms intended to belittle others while making themselves feel powerful. Since I have been working as a bartender, I have had to deal with quite a few people who use offensive language towards me. Sometimes they just do not realize that I do take offense at what they say. One man came in and said, "Who's the new barmaid?" Others have called me a "great gal" or "babe." Perhaps this is acceptable language in their minds, but I do not consider myself a "gal" or a "babe." Most of the customers who use these terms are older, rich men who probably find it cute or amusing to see a woman working as bartender. Instead of making me feel inferior, however, this language only serves to reinforce my own sense of worth, and it forces me to look at the person using these sexist terms as someone of lesser intelligence.

Exercise 29.3 Identifying and Using Figurative Language

This exercise could be completed individually or in groups; the second portion is particularly well suited to group work.

1. personification
2. allusion
3. metaphor
4. hyperbole
5. simile
6. metaphor
7. irony
8. litotes
9. irony
10. simile

Sample sentences are given below. If you are unsure about your answers, check with your instructor.

1. A gentle breeze blew through the forest, and high above our heads, the trees whispered to each other. (personification)
2. Some conservatives believe that socialism is but a short step away from an Orwellian nightmare of total state control. (allusion)
3. A ghost in the gathering fog, the old fisherman slowly rowed away from the wharf. (metaphor)
4. We've gone over your proposal a thousand times, and we still cannot justify spending so much money on a study comparing brands of raspberry jam. (hyperbole)

5. The old mansion's broken windows were like rows of blinded eyes. (simile)
6. Your dog is welcome to chew on my Persian carpet any time. (irony)
7. If I win the lottery, I won't have to worry about my phone bill any more. (litotes)

Exercise 29.4 Identifying Familiar and Informal Language

Sample analysis:

The passage contains several words and phrases which are too informal or familiar for academic writing. The opening of the very first sentence is one example. Other excessively informal terms or phrases include tube, big bucks, lousy, peanuts, and the like. All these terms might be appropriate for informal conversation, but suggest a lack of careful thought when presented as information or argument intended for an academic audience. In addition, the passage punctuates straight arrow as a complete sentence. Such nonstandard grammar also tends to undermine the credibility of this writing. In short, this passage would not be appropriate for formal writing; its informality would lead readers to dismiss it rather than take it seriously.

Exercise 29.5 Revising Familiar and Informal Language

A sample revision is given below.

Opponents of the independent candidate Kehler do not have solid grounds for argument. Though his sincerity is clear (even on television), still they question it. More importantly, Kehler favours raising the minimum wage and giving fast-food workers like my sister fairer compensation. Kehler's enthusiasm and dedication would make him a strong leader.

Exercise 29.6 Analysing the Use of Technical Language

Here is a sample analysis:

This passage does use vocabulary that will confuse many university readers. Terms such as "kerning," "typography," and "WYSIWYG" will simply puzzle some readers, hence creating confusion rather than clear communication. Even if some readers do have a vague idea of what typography is and what desktop publishing is, few will have any clue as to the specialized meaning of "widows and orphans." This writer needs to think harder about audience and then add explanations to this prose.

191

— 30 —
Considering Diction

Exercise 30.1   Balancing General and Specific Diction in a Paragraph

Sample paragraph on a pet peeve:

I am consistently irked by technology that fails. When the toaster's silvery ribbons fail to go red hot, I go red hot. Suddenly the toast that I would have eaten absentmindedly over the front page of the paper now becomes a priceless commodity; denied this culinary delight, I lose all interest in any kind of breakfast. Last winter my car ran faithfully all through November and half way through December. Sure, the battery seemed to be getting a bit weak, but it worked. Then one frigid morning, only days before Christmas, I turned the ignition key and heard only a sickening click. No grinding of starter motor. No headlights stabbing the darkness. Only the radio worked, feebly. One Thanksgiving after a long and involved meal served to assorted guests and relatives, our dishwasher decided to blow a gasket, turning a perfectly normal kitchen floor into a wet and treacherously slippery surface. Yes, I know all our gadgets and laboursavers will eventually break or wear out, but that doesn't mean I forgive them.

Assignment 30A   Choosing Language Appropriate to Academic Essays

Your revisions may be different from the samples given below.

1. Moby Dick's enormous size was matched only by Ahab's obsessive desire to destroy him.
2. The accused is charged with wilfully destroying another person's apartment.
3. This essay will refute Mr. Buckley's argument.
4. Every election year, public service announcements urge us all to go to our respective polling stations and make our preferences known.
5. Constance Beresford-Howe's much-loved novel, *The Book of Eve*, focuses on a 65-year-old woman and what happens after she leaves her husband to live on her own.

Assignment 30B   Checking for Denotative Errors

2. allusion/Correct word: illusion
3. disposition/Correct word: deposition
4. C
5. purport/Correct word: report
6. conscience/Correct word: conscious
7. C
8. report/Correct word: purport
9. illusion/Correct word: allusion
10. deposition/Correct word: disposition

The words below can be listed in any order.

Word List:
conscious
allusion
disposition
purport
conscience
report
illusion
deposition

Assignment 30C Understanding Connotative Meanings

Sample answers are given below.

1. He's crazy if he thinks he's going to borrow my car again.
   Mr. Q's psychotic symptoms prevent him from managing his own affairs.
2. My friend is so cheap she saves the cups she gets at fast food restaurants.
   Paying only half price for that sweatshirt was a real bargain.
3. Though long past his prime, the gelding looked spry this morning.
   The mime was nimble with both feet and hands.
4. The hurricane's destruction cost insurance companies several million dollars.
   Disposal company rates are determined by the county council
5. For most recipes, imitation vanilla works just as well as vanilla extract.
   Caught trying to pass bogus $20 bills, the two suspects were later accused of ten counts of forgery.

   Here are the words that should have been underlined and possible revisions.

6. crackpots claim
   Rewrite: News media spokespersons assert that their news reports are fair and impartial.
7. keep screaming
   Rewrite: Pro-choice sympathizers consistently assert that a ban on abortion would drive abortion out of hospitals and into back alleys.
8. mob/yelling/jabbing
   Rewrite: A large group of chanting, sign-waving protesters appeared.
9. keep whining/bums/crazies
   Rewrite: Liberal-minded politicians consistently focus attention on the homeless, the mentally ill, and the unemployed.
10. ladies landed seats
    Rewrite: Only recently have women been appointed Supreme Court justices.

─── 31 ───
Working on Vocabulary

Exercise 31.1   Using Word Roots

1. script 2. photograph 3. terrain 4. biography 5. manual 6. psychologist 7. television

Exercise 31.2   Composing Using Word Roots

Sample sentences:

I know an audiophile who is particularly sensitive to imperfections in sound systems.
Roots: audi (to hear), phil (love), sens (to feel)
Even over the telephone, your benevolence and sympathy have been a source of comfort.
Roots: tele (far away), bene (good), path (to feel)
I cannot describe our first vision of that territory!
Roots: scribe (write), vis (see), terr (ground)
This portable missile is manually launched.
Roots: port (to carry), miss (to send), manu (hand)

Exercise 31.3   Using Prefixes and Suffixes

Sample answers are given below.

1. remit
   Literal Meaning: again + send/Common Meaning: to send back or send by return mail
   Please remit the $25.00 owed on your bill.
2. biped
   Literal meaning: two + foot/Common meaning: an animal with two feet
   A human being is a biped.
3. convene
   Literal meaning: with + come/Common meeting: to call together
   The president convened the directors' meeting.
4. prescribe
   Literal meaning: before + write/Common meaning: to indicate as a guide or rule
   The doctor prescribed a muscle relaxant and rest.
5. educate
   Literal meaning: out of + lead/Common Meaning: to school or teach
   Good teachers educate by provoking us to teach ourselves.

Here are some sample new words and sentences:

1. Sentence #1: The surgeons operate tomorrow.

194

Root + suffix: operation

Sentence #2: We all know the operation will be a success.

2. Sentence #1: She gave a false answer for the second question.

Root + suffix: falsify

Sentence #2: She said she was forced to falsify the documents.

3. Sentence #1: My good friend Lee lives in Whitehorse.

Root + suffix: friendship

Sentence #2: Our friendship has lasted over fifteen years.

4. Sentence #1: This book's coverage is very broad.

Root + suffix: broaden

Sentence #2: They plan to broaden their approach.

5. Sentence #1: Alfred Hitchcock's movies almost always employed suspense.

New word: suspenseful

The suspenseful hours dragged on as rescuers toiled in the mine.

6. Sentence #1: The truck pulled into the right lane and allowed us to pass.

New word: passable

Sentence #2: Snowplows worked all night to make the road passable.

Exercise 31.4 Determining Meaning from Context

This exercise is designed to be completed individually. No answers can be supplied.

Using Dictionaries

EXERCISE 32.1 Consulting Basic Dictionary Entries

Note: No. 6 (mannequin) and no. 9 (accoutrement) have more than one correct spelling, yours may differ from the sample below and still be correct.

1. pre*cede
2. hors d'oeuvre (no syllabic breaks)
3. pres*tig*ious
4. in*vei*gle
5. pin*head (one word)
6. man*ne*quin
7. nec*es*sar*y
8. me*di*ate
9. ac*cou*tre*ment

In each case below, the list of possible synonyms is by no means exhaustive.

10. physical, corporeal, important, cloth
11. claim, require, exact
12. brighten, clarify, instruct
13. path, route, course
14. wrathful, irate, furious
15. promise, command, term
16. annoyed, pestered, irritated
17. rank, arrange, spot
18. cold, unfriendly
[Note that #22 and #23 carry several meanings even for the same part of speech.]
19. concrete
    kŏn-krēt′, kŏn′krēt
    adjective, noun, verb
    as adjective: relating to a specific thing or instance
    as noun: a construction material made of rock, sand, and cement
    as verb: to form into a mass, to build or cover with concrete.
20. delegate
    dĕl′ĭ-gāt, -gĭt
    noun, verb
    as noun: a person authorized to act on behalf of another.
    as verb: to authorize and send another as one's representative, to transfer authority to a subordinate.
21. animate
    ăn′ə-māt, ăn′ə-mĭt

tr. verb, adjective

as verb: to give life, to fill with spirit, to enliven.

as adjective: possessing life, lively, vigorous, seeming to possess life.

22. interest

ĭn'trĭst, t ər-ĭst, -trĕst

noun, tr. verb

as noun: a feeling of curiosity, also a legal share in something, also a bank charge, also a bonus beyond the expected.

as verb: to make curious or arouse the attention of.

23. converse

kən-vûrs', kŏn'vûrs

intr. verb, noun, adjective

as verb: to talk.

as noun: spoken interchange, discussion, also (in mathematics) something reversed or made opposite, and (in logic) a proposition obtained by conversion.

as adjective: reversed or contrary.

24. advertisement

'ad-vər-'tīz-mənt; əd-'vərt'əz-mənt, ə-smənt

noun

the act or process of advertising, or a public notice; esp. one published in the press or broadcast over the air.

25. advocate

'ad-və-kət, -,kāt

noun, transitive verb

as noun: one that pleads the cause of another.

as transitive verb: to plead in favour of; support.

26. recluse

'rek-,lüs, ri-klüs, 'rek-,lüz

adjective, noun

as adjective: marked by withdrawal from society.

as noun: a person who leads a secluded life.

27. amortize

'am-ər-,tīz,ə-'mor-

transitive verb

to provide for the gradual extinguishment of (as a mortgage) usu. by contribution to a sinking fund at the time of each periodic payment.

Exercise 32.2   Using a Thesaurus

In each case, the list of synonyms provided below is not exhaustive.

1. *satiate*: quench, satisfy, gorge, glut, sate
2. *reject*: renounce, exclude, refuse, deny, disallow
3. *obscure*: unclear, unknown, incoherent, remote, doubtful
4. *pacify*: ease, settle, placate, quiet, calm
5. *strength*: power, might, force, validity, cogency

Exercise 32.3 Using the Library's Special Dictionaries

Sample answers to the numbered questions follow.

1. In popular usage, there is very little difference. Both terms indicate an untrue and malicious imputation. However, legally <u>slander</u> means such an imputation uttered out loud or by means of gesture; thus <u>slander</u> exists in an impermanent form. <u>Libel</u> refers to such an imputation in some sort of permanent form, typically either printed or broadcast.
2. No, it is not permissible to allude to someone by name. In an allusion, that which is being alluded to is never named.
3. <u>Mendacity</u> refers to the acts of a liar, whereas <u>mendicity</u> refers to the acts of a beggar.

— 33 —
Mastering Spelling

Exercise 33.1   Noting Spelling Uncertainties as You Write and Proofreading for Misspellings

Here is a sample freewrite, with possibly misspelled words underlined:

When I think about diet and health, I think about eating the right foods to stay healthy like vegtables and salads and fruit, etc. Ice cream and cake are probably my biggest weaknesses. I also try to exercise at least four times a week by going to the health club and rideing a stationery bike for arobic exercise, doing calistenics,and then using the Nautilous machines. So a combination of good eating habits and exercise is best. I also try to eat a lot of pasta (it's good for you and cheap too). The other thing is to get enough rest — which is definately something I need to work on — and drink a lot of water.

Correct spellings are in parentheses:

vegtables (vegetables)
rideing (riding)
stationery (stationary)
arobic (aerobic)
calistenics (calisthenics)
Nautilous (Nautilus)
definately (definitely)

Exercise 33.2   Reviewing Commonly Misspelled Words

1. Word: argument
   In the past: I've misspelled this word by adding an *e* after the *u*.
   Sentence: Do we have to have this argument in a public place?
2. Word: occurred
   In the past: I've misspelled this word by dropping one of the *r*'s.
   Sentence: The power outage occurred in the middle of dinner.
3. Word: until
   In the past: I've added an extra *t*.
   Sentence: She waited until the rain stopped before going outside to work in the garden.
4. Word: roommate
   In the past: I've dropped one of the *m*'s.
   Sentence: My brother's roommate is one of the messiest people I have ever met.
5. Word: professor
   In the past: I've misspelled this word by adding an *f*.
   Sentence: Do you know which professor is teaching the course on the politics of French Canada?

Exercise 33.3   Distinguishing between Homonyms and other Similar-sounding Words

Sample answers are given below.

1A. Eric was frustrated because he hated to lose.
 B. The loose chain on my bicycle finally slipped off the sprocket.
2A. Amy did not know who broke the window, but her conscience was clear.
 B. When the paramedics arrived, the patient was conscious and lucid.
3A. The submarine's descent was gradual and imperceptible.
 B. Totalitarian governments tolerate no dissent from any politicians.
4A. Alice said, "I accept your apology."
 B. That new blouse is beautiful, except for the colour.
5A. Tom used the extension ladder to climb onto the roof.
 B. Of the two television shows you mentioned, I prefer the latter.
6A. The device on his car visor is for activating the automatic garage door opener.
 B. When we were children, we spent days trying to devise a foolproof system for sneaking cookies from the pantry.
7A. Lucy, who designs and sews her own clothes, is always getting compliments on her fashion sense.
 B. The waiter suggested a hearty red wine to complement our meal.
8A. Jason has a mysterious past; he doesn't like to discuss his family or his childhood.
 B. The Porsche passed our Chevy in a cloud of dust and disappeared around the bend.
9A. The principal reason we chose this campsite was its proximity to the lake.
 B. I agree with you in principle, but I don't believe your solution to the problem is workable.
10A. The students' council met to decide whether to allot funds for a visiting speaker or for a video dance.
 B. Fitness experts usually counsel beginners to start slowly so as to avoid injury and fatigue.

Exercise 33.4   Using Rules for *i* before *e* and for Some Suffixes

1. Misspelled words: careful, neither, received
2. Misspelled words: usually, grief
3. Misspelled words: sharing, diplomatically
4. Misspelled words: Having
5. Misspelled words: courageous, truly

Exercise 33.5   Using Additional Suffix Rules

1. employer [keep the *y* when *y* follows a vowel]
2. conducting [final consonant preceded by a consonant, do not double]
3. referring [in words of more than one syllable, double the final consonant when a single vowel precedes the final consonant and the sounded stress falls on the last syllable of the original word once the suffix has been added.]
4. studied [change the *y* to *i* when it follows a consonant.]
5. controllable [in words of more than one syllable, double the final consonant when a single vowel precedes the final consonant and the sounded stress falls on the last syllable of the original word once the suffix has been added.]

Assignment 33A Constructing a Personal Spelling Chart

This exercise is to be done on an individual basis. No answers are supplied.

Assignment 33B Proofreading for Spelling Errors

A list of the misspelled words and their correct spellings follows. Note that the word *omelet* is spelled correctly, but may also be spelled *omelette*.

any thing	anything
knowlege	knowledge
patients	patience
wether	whether
sewwing	sewing
desining	designing
useing	using
culinery	culinary
grate	great
prefect	perfect
makeing	making
youself	yourself
woud	would
cabanet	cabinet
consumeing	consuming
privite	private
expectted	expected
keepping	keeping
maintaning	maintaining
stanards	standards
controling	controlling
tempter	temper
lern	learn
improove	improve
wil	will
estimateion	estimation
talence	talents

— 34 —
Using Commas

Exercise 34.1 Using Commas After Introductory Elements

Commas have been added to the paragraph below in a fashion consistent with the chapter's explanations; you may make your own decision about, for example, the need for a comma following "For instance" in the last sentence of the first paragraph.

Since its introduction by Parker Brothers in 1935, Monopoly has taught several generations its unique version of capitalism. In this game of wish-fulfilment‚ everyone starts with ready cash. Decision-making is reduced to a roll of the dice. And wonder of wonders‚ nobody works. Instead‚ gameplayers simply wait to arrive again at Go in order to collect another $200. Besides a life of leisure‚ Monopoly players come to expect remarkably depressed real estate prices. For instance, the Mediterranean Avenue property still sells for only $60.

Exercise 34.2 Using Commas to Set Off Nonrestrictive Information

The material to be underlined and the correct labels and comma usage are listed below.

1. wearing the striped swimsuit: restrictive; no commas added
2. preferably some kind of melon: nonrestrictive information; commas added
3. which is carried locally on Channel 27: nonrestrictive information; commas added
4. that measure less than six inches: restrictive; no commas added
5. which have grown increasingly rare in recent years: nonrestrictive information; commas added

Exercise 34.3 Using Commas with Quotations

1. add comma after *said*
2. add commas after *Canadians* and *said* [comma after Canadians falls within the quotation marks]
3. cross out comma after *say*
4. cross out comma after *that*
5. add comma after *Yesterday* [comma falls within the quotation marks]

Exercise 34.4 Omitting Commas between Subjects and Verbs and between Verbs and Objects

Commas should be crossed out in the following places:

first sentence: after *Consider*

3. The October 1987 stock market crash drove many small investors out of the market.
4. The mailing address for Nelson Canada is 1120 Birchmount Road, Scarborough, Ontario M1K 5G4.
5. Hey, stop ogling that construction worker!

Here are the revised sentences with commas added.

6. Rak, could you read over the third paragraph and tell me what it says to you?
7. Laura Williams, M.D., can be found in office 228 on the second floor.
8. Now we stitch the seam, right?
9. Last year, I am sorry to say, six elms had to be destroyed due to Dutch elm disease.
10. Your rough draft is due Friday, October 28.

Assignment 34D   Distinguishing between Restrictive and Nonrestrictive Sentence Elements

1. that have been mistreated by their owners/restrictive
   no commas added
2. marked down for this special sale/restrictive
   no commas added
3. some with only the clothes on their backs/nonrestrictive
   commas added after *evacuees* and *backs*
4. who is an accomplished poet and teacher/restrictive
   no commas added
5. a field that has grown in recent years/nonrestrictive
   commas added after *administration* and *years*

Assignment 34E   Omitting Unnecessary Commas

Here are the commas that should be crossed out.

1. after *year*
2. after *delicious*
3. after *make*, after *pies*, after *and*
4. C
5. after *pool*
6. after *Munro*

Assignment 34F   Using Commas Correctly

Your answers may vary slightly from those provided below. Check with your instructor if you are unsure of your sentences.

1. Carpentry and needlework require patience.
2. Designing your own clothes, which can be quite rewarding, is not as hard as some people think.
3. Some writers like to read a bit before writing, some make copious notes to themselves, some are too terrified to do anything, and some just sit down and start writing whatever comes to mind.
4. On those April mornings after a heavy rain, you wake up in Vancouver, you look out the window, and it's so clear that you understand why everyone moved here.

5. The orientation classes that begin Monday morning at 9:00 are designed for transfer students only.
   or
   The orientation classes designed exclusively for transfer students begin on Monday morning at 9:00.
6. The typewriter is fast, and it produces professional-looking documents.
7. The typewriter is fast, and it produces professional-looking documents, but I still prefer to hand-write my memos.
8. We have confirmed our reservations, we have taken the dog to the neighbours, and the car is packed, so let's go.
9. Margaret tripped going down the stairs, but she did not lose consciousness.
10. You love golf, you enjoy the companionship, and you admire the lush landscape, yet you play maybe once a year.

Using Semicolons

Exercise 35.1 Revising Using Semicolons

Revisions here may vary considerably; a sample revision is given below.

Recovering alcoholics are some of the nicest people you'd ever want to meet; unfortunately, they also tell some of the saddest, most distressing stories. Many of them come from alcoholic families. Maybe the father was a functional, low-profile drinker for years; maybe the mother drank during the day and locked her own kids out of the house because she couldn't stand their noise. In some cases, the kids also suffered from sexual abuse or other physical violence. When these kids reached adulthood, they hid their hurt in a bottle. Some of them didn't wait for adulthood; some drank right along with their parents.

Untreated alcoholics believe they have every reason to drink. Through treatment, however, they come to learn that no reason is a good enough reason for them to drink. For the alcoholic, that beer or wine or gin makes every problem worse; without fail, excessive, compulsive drinking creates new problems. Staying clean and sober doesn't do away with the alcoholic's problems, but it does eliminate one pressing, overpowering difficulty. The sober alcoholic then has at least the opportunity to deal with other problems. Recovery isn't easy, nor is it ever complete. But with family support and the help of organizations like Alcoholics Anonymous, people do dry out; families do get better.

Assignment 35A Using Semicolons to Link Independent Clauses

1. C
2. My current work-study job ends in two weeks; I'll need to find a new position starting next term.
3. Please save your questions for the end of the presentation if you don't understand.
4. For four glorious but underpaid weeks, I'll be working in Jasper this summer.
5. Swinging the door open quietly, the two police officers surprised a young burglar as he worked to disconnect the cable wire from the Tuckers' colour television.
6. The invitation distinctly said R.S.V.P.; even so, we lost the invitation and never properly responded.
7. Monday's U.S. Open tennis tournament was rained out; however, play is scheduled to resume Tuesday.
8. C
9. Raspberries, which are my favourite fresh fruit, ripen in late June and early July; in addition, some years there's a later, smaller crop in September.

Your combinations may vary from the samples provided below.

10. If you lose your office key, then see if it has been turned in at the front security desk; a replacement key costs $10.
11. Although some people think of wallpaper hanging as a do-it-yourself project, we tried it; we now think of wallpaper hanging as a project for professionals only.

12. I'll meet your train at the downtown station; look for the woman standing under the dark blue umbrella and carrying a tan briefcase.

13. There are fewer drive-in theatres than there once were; for example, the Imperial Drive-In has been demolished for a shopping mall.

— 36 —
Using End Punctuation

Exercise 36.1   Using Periods to Signal the Ends of Sentences

Periods should appear after the following words:

first sentence: after *sentence*
second sentence: after *sentence*
third sentence: after *once*
fourth sentence: after *task*
fifth sentence: after *read*

Exercise 36.2   Proofreading and Revising End-Punctuation Errors

Punctuation changes have been indicated above the line.

Most people think of jogging as a solitary activity I'll grant that most of the time it is exactly that.

But occasionally something unusual happens. Once a Winnebago with strange licence plates swerved

across the centre line and stopped right in front of me? I swerved too, trying not to break stride, only

to hear a rather shrill voice yell "Wait a minute, honey hey, we need to talk to you. I stopped I can't

help it if my parents taught me to be polite "Son," the driver said, "we're touring Canada, and I'm

afraid we're just a little bit lost". As it turned out, they were looking for an address in the

southeastern part of town; however, they were driving around on streets all clearly labelled as

northwest they never noticed (or at least never acknowledged) that I was beet red in the face, sweaty,

and scowling. I suppose they figured they were being polite, too.

Another time a kid with a flat bicycle tire ran along beside me for fifty metres or so, saying,

"Mister, you got ten dollars I can borrow. My tire's flat you got a dime so I can call my mom." He

didn't notice that my jogging shorts had no pockets. Of course, when I got home and told my kids

about the bicycle rider's plight, they could hardly believe it "Did that guy really expect you to have

ten dollars, one asked? And said the other, "Did he really think you'd give it to him even if you had it"? All I could do was answer with a shrug. I hadn't taken the requests too seriously. I'd been too busy trying to breathe on a regular basis.

Assignment 36A   Identifying and Correcting End-Punctuation Errors

1. Didn't I say "Either clean up your room, or there'll be no dessert after dinner"?
2. Was it in sixth grade that we first studied Canadian history? fifth grade?
3. C
4. "Have you heard the one about the tourist and the barber?" he asked.
5. Did you just say "What time is it?"
6. "Yes, I asked you what time it was."
7. "Olga, did Beth invite you over after school?" she asked.
8. C
9. My opponent has posed an interesting question: "Should Canada just become a neutral country like Switzerland?
10. C
11. What, exactly, do you want?
12. What do you mean by coming in here and telling me to leave the room?

Using Apostrophes

Assignment 37A   Using Apostrophes to Signal Possession

1. The antenna's guy wires were snapped by the wind.
2. Your children's dresses look very pretty.
3. The Stratford Festival's poster hung on his wall. (the 's here is optional)
4. The piano's finish was cracked and peeling.
5. Let's order another box of our typewriter's ribbons. (*or* of typewriter ribbons)
6. Sean's poster and Janet's poster have both been chosen as winners.
   or
   Sean's and Janet's posters have both been chosen as winners.
7. It sounds like your station wagon's muffler needs to be replaced.
8. Its paint was scratched in the accident.
9. The voters' choices have been made.
10. My paper was turned in on time.
11. It's an important decision.
12. Yes, I think that's his coat over there on the chair.

Assignment 37B   Using Apostrophes to Create Contractions

Although in most cases below, the appropriate form is clear enough from context, a few cases could be debated. A suggested answer has been provided in each case. Your rewritten sentences, however, should correspond to those below.

1. Rewrite: Shouldn't we have stopped at the market for more milk?
   More appropriate version: <u>contraction</u>
2. Rewrite: You've been listening to several people as they've described how the United Way has helped them; now won't you please take out your chequebooks and help your neighbours?
   More appropriate version: <u>contraction</u>
3. Rewrite: That guy who has been giving you a ride after class called at about nine of the clock.
   More appropriate version: <u>contraction</u>
4. Rewrite: Some critics argue that Timothy Findley will be remembered as one of the best novelists of the 1980s. [1980's is also correct]
   More appropriate version: <u>full form</u>
5. Rewrite: The clothes I'm washing now didn't really get too dirty.
   More appropriate version: <u>contraction</u>
6. Rewrite: For the test you will be taking on Monday, you are required to have a pencil with a No. 2 lead.
   More appropriate version: <u>full form</u>
7. Rewrite: The judge will be available to meet with you once court adjourns.
   More appropriate version: <u>full form</u>

8. Rewrite: The distributor informs me that your order hasn't received its required approval from the business office.
   More appropriate version: either one; see note above
9. Rewrite: Whoever is responsible for an accident has the legal obligation to compensate any injured parties.
   More appropriate version: full form
10. You have been told over and over that you should not play in the street.
    More appropriate version: full form

Assignment 37C   Using Apostrophes

With the end of summer, many students begin to think about registration for the new term, course schedule booklets become hot items, and the rumour mill churns into operation. Whose [Who's] had whom in which classes? Hows [How's] so and so in history? How many As [A's] did so and so give in psychology last term?

Anyone heard how many essays there'll be? Hallways buzz and the tables in the student union fill up once more. All over campus, department secretaries [secretaries'] patience wears thin even as they politely answer question's [questions] about adding or dropping classes, changing majors, and so forth. Faculty members [members'] offices echo with the sound of typewriters or computer printers. Meanwhile, the bookstores [bookstore's] lines stretch back from the cash registers all the way to the next years [year's] calendars, which are already on sale. Returning student's [students] sometimes find its [it's] not possible to walk across campus without running into an old acquaintance. They keep "Hows [How's] it going?" and "What's new?" on the tip of the tongue.

By late November, the trees dont [don't] rustle; theyre [they're] bare. Maybe its [it's] even snowed already. Snow or not, much of the terms [term's] earlier anticipation has been replaced by some quite specific challenges: the paper due tomorrow, the necessary B on the next test (after two Cs [C's] and a C-), the upcoming oral presentation in French. But in August or September, all thats [that's] in the future. The sun shines, the summers [summer's] moneys [money's] in the bank, and everyone secretly believes that again this term the registrars [registrar's] computer will be friendly.

Using Quotation Marks

Exercise 38.1   Varying Quotation Format According to Length

Here is a sample quotation from a poem:

Gerard Manley Hopkins uses language like no other poet I have read. His poem "God's Grandeur" is a good example. It starts: "The world is charged with the grandeur of God./It will flame out, like shining from shook foil."

Here is a sample quotation from the handbook:

I have always had trouble with knowing when to use a singular form of the verb and when to use a plural, especially when the subject has other words near it or attached to it. I found the following suggestion, from page 337 of the handbook, helpful:

If you know that you have problems with subject-verb agreement when the simple subject and the verb are separated by other words, proofread each of your sentences to identify the simple subject and the verb. Then mentally delete the intervening words, if any, to make sure that the subject and verb agree in number and person.

Exercise 38.2   Using Quotation Marks to Signal Dialogue

A short example is given below.

"You need any more pop? I'm going to the kitchen."
"No, thanks, I still have some here. I could use some crackers or maybe a ham sandwich with lettuce and a little bit of mustard."
"You don't want much, do you?"
"You asked."
"Listen, instead of going into the kitchen, I'd like to hear about your date last night."
"Oh, that."
"Well?"
"It's so weird to be dating at my age."

Assignment 38A   Using Quotation Marks to Signal Direct Quotation

1. "Ultimately, our differences with management may result in the need to strike"; the crowd shifted uneasily at those words.
2. "I'm going outside for some fresh air," said Barb as she put on her sweater, "but I'll only be a few minutes."
3. Has everyone been informed that Ms. Jenkins said "For the duration of these training seminars, there will be no absences"?
4. "I could not believe the condition of my hometown," he wrote.
5. Oscar Wilde didn't say "The shallow never know themselves"; he said, "Only the shallow know themselves."

Only sentences with direct quotations are reprinted here.

6. indirect
7. After a tornado ripped through her house, a tearful Alberta woman said, "We're here today only because God held us in his hand; that's all I can say."
   direct
8. "The Beast destroyed my brief peace" is the first sentence of Guy Vanderhaeghe's *My Present Age*.
   direct
9. indirect
10. indirect

Assignment 38B   Using Quotation Marks Correctly

1. "Listen," screamed the television character, "if you say 'I'm going to leave you' one more time, I'll ask you to leave!"
2. George Orwell's essay "Politics and the English Language" deserves its place in the anthologies.
3. "The episode I enjoyed most," she said, "was the one titled 'Atomic Shakespeare'; it was inventive and funny."
4. "Buddhist Economics" is not a chapter title you'll find in too many textbooks.
5. "As I was telling you, he sat there in his library, sipped his drink, and said, 'I find it delightfully reassuring to live amongst all these words.'"
6. C
7. "Did I tell you," he said, "that when Cary got here, the first thing she asked was 'Well, are the hills alive with the sound of music?'"
8. The opening line of her parody read, "It was Pee-wee Herman who said 'Give me liberty, but not bad breath.'"
9. C
10. C

Assignment 38C   Identifying and Correcting Errors with Quotation Marks

One of the best kept secrets about poetry is that reading it can be a wonderful, benign addiction. Poems, like anything else handmade, reflect their makers; they are as strange, exotic, thought-provoking, and beautiful as people. Who can deny a rush of adrenaline at taking a deep breath (a really deep breath) and saying (almost singing) some of the most gorgeous sounds in English:

Now as I was young and easy under the apple boughs
About the lilting house and happy as the grass was green,
   The night above the dingle starry,
     Time let me hail and climb
   Golden in the heydays of his eyes,
And honoured among wagons I was prince of the apple towns
And once below a time I lordly had the trees and leaves
    Trail with daisies and barley
   Down the rivers of the windfall light.

So goes the opening stanza of Dylan Thomas's "Fern Hill." Skeptics might say, "Even if we grant that the language of 'Fern Hill' is indeed gorgeous, as you say, it is also virtually impossible to follow."

Ah, pity the skeptics; they have an adversarial relationship with the world. "Fern Hill" is difficult only for readers who ask that it transmit its content as a newspaper does. Newspapers are read for their information. They're written to be read easily, quickly. The sentences are short, and individually they are forgettable. Who recalls last week's headlines? In contrast, "Poetry," said Ezra Pound, "is news that stays news."

The truth is, "Fern Hill" is made to be read slowly and even inquisitively. How, after all, can a house be called "lilting"? The word has more to do with song than with architecture. Could someone have been singing? How happy is "happy as the grass was green"? It's as happy as the night is starry. Is the pun on "heydays" (hay days) intentional? What can it mean to be "prince of the apple towns"? Could apple towns be rows of apple trees — an orchard? Does that tie in with the "windfall" of the last line?

And what does this add up to? Doesn't it add up to an intensity of feeling that makes the experience ours even though it's not? We don't know that farm, except we do. We've seen the imaginations of children; we've seen how they become queens or kings of their bedrooms, their toys, their dolls. The speaker in "Fern Hill" is prince of it all. The speaker owned that farm, that time, and owns it still.

What about the odd shape of "Fern Hill" on the page? Why insist on such an arrangement? Why is the second stanza arranged identically to the first? And how is it that Thomas could ensure that the first line of the second stanza contains precisely the same number of syllables as the first line of the first stanza? The same correspondence is true for the second lines of each stanza, and the third lines, and so on until the fifth stanza, which changes the pattern somewhat. What astonishing union of content and form are we looking at here?

Actually, "Fern Hill" is childhood distilled; all the frustrations and angers have been boiled away. What's left is an awe-inspiring precision of language and feeling. What's left is the exhilaration of childhood as time in the Garden of Eden, "it was all/Shining, it was Adam and maiden,/The sky gathered again/And the sun grew round that very day." If poems are indeed an addiction, they must be the very best kind.

Using Other Punctuation Marks

Exercise 39.1 Using Parentheses and Brackets

1. That mantel clock (made in Germany in 1888) has been in the family since my father's grand-mother brought it over with her in 1901.
2. Either (1) we propose our modifications now, or (2) we wait for the final set of engineering results and risk a production failure.
3. C
4. Touring the Fortress of Louisbourg (in Cape Breton, Nova Scotia) gives you an idea of how French settlers lived in the mid-eighteenth century.
5. C

Exercise 39.2 Revising to Ensure Correct Use of Parentheses

As a general guideline, your passages should probably not contain more than one parenthetical statement. Here is a sample revision of each passage:

1. *Chatelaine* magazine has named Brandon, Manitoba one of the ten best Canadian cities to live in. Although it does not boast high average salaries, Brandon does have a low unemployment rate (5.9 percent). It also has an attractive cost of living; for example, $75,000 buys a new three-bedroom bungalow. With a population of around 40,000, Brandon is a small city, which contributes to the sense of community that residents enjoy. Because the Canada Winter Games were held there in 1979, Brandon has exceptional recreational facilities for a city its size. Brandon University's school of music and the arts centre that was recently built downtown both contribute to the cultural flavour of this appealing city.

2. Our car was approaching the intersection from the west, and Judy was driving. Maybe we weren't paying close attention (since we were arguing about which movie we were going to see). At that point, somebody, maybe Judy, yelled "No!" She began to swerve to the right to get out of the way, but the station wagon hit our front end behind the left wheel. As metal crunched and we spun around, it all seemed to be happening in slow motion.

Assignment 39A Using Dashes

1. Few recognize the name Sarah Josepha Hale — many know her poem entitled "Mary Had a Little Lamb."
2. Several kinds of lace — among them Alencon, Honiton, and Maltese — take their names from their place of origin.
3. We'll send a postcard when we arrive in Banff — if we remember.
4. Their sophistication, their perceptual abilities, even how they feel about themselves — children's pictures can tell us much about the children who drew them.
5. Your papers should be finished — the deadline is Friday at noon — and placed in the envelope on Professor Cook's office door.

6. Paul Klee—graphic artist, painter, and art theorist—remains an influential presence for contemporary artists even though he died some fifty years ago.
7. Parents should act like parents—not like squabbling children.
8. Twice Sir John A. Macdonald served as Prime Minister of Canada—from 1867 to 1873 and from 1878 to 1891.
9. Famous, Italian-born, and still remembered for her Milan debut in 1953—Renata Scotto is particularly recognized today for her performances of Puccini's *Madame Butterfly*.
10. Escape your troubles, travel without ever leaving your chair, save your money—visit your local library and read.

Assignment 39B   Using Colons

1. You're supposed to bring the condiments: mustard, ketchup, relish, dill pickles, and mayonnaise.
2. Bill's decision was a difficult one, but he stuck to it: he quit smoking for good.
3. Judith Fingard wrote a book entitled *Jack in Port: Sailortowns of Eastern Canada*.
4. I like the Book of Proverbs, especially Chapter 12:8.
5. The scout troop packed what seemed like a ton of gear into the van: four tents, a dozen sleeping bags, three propane stoves (with propane bottles), food for two nights, ropes, craft projects, and the troop flag.
6. Leonid Telyatnikov has done something he hopes no one else will have to do: he has commanded a fire crew attempting to extinguish a nuclear reactor fire.
7. Insomniacs who turn to late-night TV for company will likely find programs on investing in real estate, quitting smoking, and thinking positively.
8. The list of Norman Jewison's movie credits includes *Moonstruck*, *Fiddler on the Roof*, *Agnes of God*, and *The Cincinnati Kid*.
9. C
10. Ukrainian-Canadians have traditionally made coloured or decorated eggs to celebrate Easter and rebirth and to have on hand as gifts for visitors.
11. We ask that you come to the test equipped with the following: at least two sharpened HB pencils, erasers, two notebooks, and scrap paper.
12. Let me just tell you this: he will not come because he disapproves of the entire outing.
13. I am annoyed, exasperated, sorely tried, and fed up.

Assignment 39C   Using Ellipses

Version using ellipsis points:

He stood in the open field,...the brightness of the coloured day surrounding him, the strong flavour of autumn once again. The cow lay on its side, trying to jerk upright every so often, falling to its side again, kicking its thick hind legs. It was bleeding very little.... Another cow stood a short distance away watching, not venturing any closer.... He felt sick as he fired,...uncertain of his aim. And he fired four times rapidly and then only live nerves twitching in a dead hide and everything was quiet. He cursed and he could not stop shaking.... But he felt he must leave it there, forget it. And then he laughed nervously as he turned away.

40

Using Capitals

Exercise 40.1 Using Capitalization for the First Word of a New Sentence

Sentence 2: *as* should be *As*, *Leading* should be *leading*.
Sentence 3: *Once* should be *once*, *you're* (the first one) should be *You're*.
Sentence 4: *when* should be *When*, *She* should be *she*, *Her* [hands] should be *her* [hands].
Sentence 5: *no* should be *No* (the first one), *She'd* should be *she'd*
Sentence 6: *she* (the second one) should be *She* (Note: This change is optional.)
Sentence 7: *her* should be *Her*
Sentence 8: *for* should be *For*
Sentence 11: *i* should be *I*
Sentence 12: *It* should be *it*
Sentence 14: *To* [learn] should be *to* [learn]

Exercise 40.2 Using Capitals for Proper Nouns and Proper Adjectives

1. *new*; part of proper name — capitalize
   Saint John; part of proper name — capitalize
   river; part of proper name — capitalize
   Population; not part of proper name — no capitalization
   Saint John, New Brunswick, lies on the Saint John River and boasts a population of over 80,000.
2. *Screen*; first word of sentence — no capitalization
   Actress; not proper noun — no capitalization
   Princess; part of title — capitalize
   Monaco; proper noun — capitalize
   North; direction not part of proper name — no capitalization
   Screen actress and later Princess of Monaco, Grace Kelly died when her car (which was headed north) left the road and plunged down an embankment.
3. *Business*; generic identification, not proper noun — no capitalization
   leaders; generic identification, not proper noun — no capitalization
   bell northern research; company name — capitalize
   Region's; generic noun not part of proper name — no capitalization
   Ottawa area business leaders consider Bell Northern Research one of the region's most important corporations.

Exercise 40.3 More Practice with Capitalizing Proper Nouns and Proper Adjectives

1. *Landlords*; generic noun, not proper name — no capitalization
   A; article preceding proper name — no capitalization
   Toronto; proper name functioning as proper adjective — capitalize
   Apartment; generic noun, not part of name — no capitalization
   Many non-natives are surprised by the rent landlords typically charge for a Toronto apartment.

2. *The*; first word of sentence — capitalize
   Division; major word in proper name — capitalize
   Of; preposition in proper name — no capitalization
   education; major word in proper name — capitalize
   The Division of Language and Literature is happy to announce that it is the recipient of a grant from the Ontario Ministry of Education.
3. *scouts*; major word in proper name — capitalize
   league; major word in proper name — capitalize
   Members; generic noun, not proper name — no capitalization
   University; generic noun functioning as adjective, not proper name — no capitalization
   Cub Scouts, Rotarians, members of the Junior Service League, and members of various university clubs joined forces yesterday to publicize the need for more blood donations.
4. *Remembrance*; name of national holiday — capitalize
   a; article not part of title — no capitalization
   saturday; day of the week — capitalize
   year; generic noun, not proper name — no capitalization
   Since Remembrance Day falls on a Saturday this year, the actual observance will be reserved for the following Monday.
5. *biblical*; exception to rule — no capitalization
   honour; not proper noun, title, or quotation — no capitalization
   the; article preceding title — no capitalization
   koran; title of religious work — capitalize
   various; adjective, not proper adjective — no capitalization
   Confucius; proper name — capitalize
   The biblical injunction to honour one's parents is echoed in the Koran and can also be found in the various sayings attributed to Confucius.

Assignment 40A   Revising for Correct Capitalization

1. If you turn west on Northwest Walnut Street, you won't miss Central School.
2. The committee member strode forward, shook the chairperson's hand, and said, "Madam Chair, I support your new procedural proposal."
3. Some wealthy business executives resign their posts in order to seek new challenges in business or education.
4. Architects have commented favourably on designs for the Royal Bank Tower, which will eventually be built on the northwest corner of Fifth Street and Alder Avenue.
5. Nova Scotia's Grand Pré National Historic Park was established to commemorate the expulsion of the town's Acadian settlers between 1755 and 1763.

Assignment 40B   Identifying and Correcting Capitalization Errors

2000 ~~n.e. main st.~~ *N.E. Main St.*
~~ottawa~~, Ontario *Ottawa*

K1V 3M9
~~january~~ 2, 1989 *January*

218

Acme Trading ~~co.~~ **Co.**

43561 Shady ~~lane~~ **Lane**

Kingston, ~~ontario~~ **Ontario**

K7L 2M4

Dear
My ~~dear~~ Friends at Acme Trading,

Are ~~You~~ **you** looking for a ~~Self-starter~~ **self-starter**—~~somOne~~ **someone** who can ~~Get~~ **get** the ~~Job Done~~ **job done**? I have had over ~~Two Years~~ **two years**

of retail experience working for Waterbeds, ~~Waterbeds~~ **Waterbeds**, & ~~waterbeds~~, Inc. During one ~~Summer~~ **summer**, I

sold over six new complete packages. I sold waterbeds as ~~Halitosis~~ **halitosis** cures, ~~Bunion~~ **bunion** relievers, and—~~o~~ **0**

yes!—headache destroyers (so long as the head of the bed was facing ~~West~~ **west**). I could sell a waterbed

to the ghost of my ~~Mother's~~ **mother's** grandmother. I could sell ice cubes on Sundays in ~~Winter~~ **winter** in the ~~yukon~~ **Yukon**.

All of this convinces me that ~~i AM Management Material~~ **I am management material**; your trainee program sounds perfect for

me. Give ~~Me~~ **me** the chance, and I'll get ~~YOU~~ **you** the results you want.

Very ~~Truly YOURS~~ **truly yours**,

41

Using Abbreviations and Numbers

Exercise 41.1 Using Abbreviations for Personal and Professional Titles

1. C
2. Father McDill
3. Dr. JoAnne Trow, or JoAnne Trow, Ph.D.
4. saint
5. professors

Exercise 41.2 Using Abbreviations with Numerals

1. @ [should be at]
2. a.m. [should be morning]
3. % [should be percent]
4. & [should be and]
5. @ [should be At]
   + [should be plus]
   = [should be equal]
6. C
7. $ [should be money (or dollars)]
8. C
9. Km [should be kilometres] hr [should be hour]

Exercise 41.3 Using Acronyms and Initial Abbreviations

Five sample abbreviations and acronyms are listed below.

1. Abbreviations/Acronym: CN
   Long form: Canadian National
   Sample sentence: I have a cousin who works as a brakeperson for CN in Montreal.
   Audience that will recognize this: most Canadians
   Audience that will not recognize this: non-Canadians
2. Abbreviation/Acronym: TDS
   Long form: total debt service
   Sample sentence: The loans officer will have to calculate your TDS before pre-approving your mortgage.
   Audience that will recognize this: bankers, mortgage brokers, real estate salespeople
   Audience that will not recognize this: anyone not familiar with money-lending
3. Abbreviation/Acronym: NAC
   Long form: National Arts Centre
   Sample sentence: My friend and I went to see David Hare's new play at the NAC last spring.

Audience that will recognize this: Ottawa area residents; members of the Canadian performing arts community

Audience that will not recognize this: people not familiar with Canadian performing arts

4. Abbreviation/Acronym: SWAP

Long form: Student Work Abroad Program

Sample sentence: Through SWAP, Randy has arranged to spend next year living and working in Australia.

Audience that will recognize this: post-secondary students

Audience that will not recognize this: those unfamiliar with post-secondary student programs

5. Abbreviation/Acronym: NAAW

Long form: National Access Awareness Week

Sample sentence: The local rehabilitation centre is booking a blind singer to perform during NAAW this year.

Audience that will recognize this: Canadians with disabilities and those working on their behalf

Audience that will not recognize this: those unfamiliar with issues concerning Canadians with disabilities

Assignment 41A   Avoiding the Misuse or Overuse of Abbreviations

Abbreviations that should be underlined are listed below. If they are inappropriate, corrected versions are given in parentheses.

1. et al. (and others)
2. Feb. (February) Pk. (Park)
3. 5/18/81 (May 18, 1981)
4. Tues. (Tuesday), Aug. (August)
5. C. (Charlotte)
6. S. (South), pop. (population)
7. R. (River), N.W.T. (Northwest Territories), Lk. (Lake)
8. yrs. (years), '69 (1969)
9. Alta. (Alberta), sq. km (square kilometres)
10. etc. (and so on)

Assignment 41B   Writing Numbers

John Ruskin, an influential nineteenth-century British writer, was born in eighteen-nineteen. *[1819]*

Allowed few toys or friends, he had a lonely childhood, and learned to amuse himself with imaginative games and with study. He published an early essay at the age of 15; *[fifteen]* before his death in nineteen hundred, *[1900]* he would publish 100s *[hundreds]* of essays and lectures on a wide range of topics from art to travel to natural history.

On April tenth, *[10]* 1848, at 4 *[four]* o'clock in the afternoon, Ruskin was married to Euphemia Gray in Perth, Scotland. He was 29 *[twenty-nine]* and she was 19. *[nineteen]* Ruskin had met Effie when she was still a child, but developed stronger feelings for her during a visit she paid to his family just 2 *[two]* years before they were

221

married. His feelings for her were not, however, of a physical nature: for the next 7 [*seven*] years, until Effie divorced him, the marriage remained unconsummated. 1 [*one*] year after the divorce, Effie married John Everett Millais, 1 [*one*] of the young artists of the Pre-Raphaelite Brotherhood, a friend and former travelling companion of the Ruskins. This marriage was different in at least one respect: Effie went on to have 8 [*eight*] children—4 [*four*] boys and 4 [*four*] girls.

— 42 —

Using Italics

Exercise 42.1 Using Italics for Foreign Words or Phrases

The Random House College Dictionary: Revised Edition (1984) has been used as the authority for the answers below.

habeas corpus [no italics] sans souci [italicize] idée fixe [italicize] ex post facto [italicize] a priori [no italics] bon mot [no italics] gemütlichkeit [italicize] glasnost [italicize] habitué [no italics] bona fide [no italics]
Sample sentences:
When the lawyer obtained a writ of habeas corpus, the defendant was released.
A *san souci* attitude is exactly what vacationers need.
She has an *idée fixe* about what constitutes proper dress.
The investigators' *ex post facto* reconstruction of the crime eventually led them to a suspect.
The jury was urged to make no a priori judgements.
When we're talking, she always comes up with the right bon mot.
Fran's *gemütlichkeit* makes her a welcome guest at parties.
Most people have welcomed the changes associated with *glasnost*.
He was a habitué of the Oxford Bar and Grill.
That, my boy, is a bona fide cutthroat trout.

Exercise 42.2 Italicizing the Names of Vehicles

These names should be underlined.

1. Bluenose
2. Hindenburg
3. (Nothing in this sentence needs underlining.)
4. Spirit of St. Louis
5. Mercury, Freedom 7

Exercise 42.3 Using Italics Sparingly for Emphasis

1. Suggests that the speaker thinks it might be excessive to ask the Johnsons to bring both hamburgers and potato salad.
2. Suggests that the scores were virtually as high as they could be.
3. The effect here is of straightforward emphasis indicating resolve and determination.

A sample sentence is provided below, with a different word italicized in each case.

Do you think baby Andrew will actually eat his *carrots*?

Analysis: The sentence suggests that baby Andrew is not fond of carrots, and that he will likely leave that part of his meal uneaten.

Do you think baby Andrew will actually *eat* his carrots?

Analysis: This sentence suggests that baby Andrew may do something else with his carrots. He may smear them on himself or throw them on the floor, but he will not likely eat them.

Assignment 42A   Using Italics for Titles and for Words, Letters, or Numbers Referred to as Such

Terms that should be underlined are listed below.

1. TV Guide's, Bonanza, Gunsmoke, The Lone Ranger
2. Messiah
3. Les Belles Soeurs
4. The Awakening
5. (Nothing should be underlined.)
6. Lady Oracle
7. Children's Digest, Chatelaine, Seventeen, Maclean's, and National Geographic
8. (Nothing should be underlined.)
9. M
10. Poetry
11. (Nothing should be underlined.)
12. Saturday Night

Exercise 43.1   Using Hyphens to Divide Words at the Ends of Lines

Some sentences below can be revised in more than one correct manner. Though only one sample answer is provided below, you can supply any revision that accurately employs the guidelines discussed in the first part of this chapter.

Incorrect hyphenations are listed below, with brief explanations.

1. sun- ny (sunny) *There should not be fewer than three letters on the second line.*
2. precipit- ation (precipi-tation) *Divide words only between syllables.*
3. unseasonab- le (unseasonable) *Never leave fewer than three letters at the beginning of a line.*
4. hur- ricane-force (hurricane-force) *Divide compound words where they join.*
5. C
6. C
7. care- er (career) *Divide words between syllables.*
8. C
9. NB- C (NBC) *Do not divide acronyms or abbreviations.*
10. C

Exercise 43.2   Using Hyphens to Clarify Meaning

Sample sentences are provided below.

1. Scientists are now able to achieve procreation in test tubes.
2. Could you re-cover my armchair in a plaid fabric?
3. For recreation, many people participate in bowling leagues.
4. To commemorate the hundredth anniversary of the composer's birthdate, a re-creation of the premiere of his first opera was staged.
5. Now re-form your clay into something entirely different.
6. The reform you advocate will be seriously considered.

Assignment 43A   Using Hyphens with Compound Words and Compound Modifiers

1. This is a brilliantly argued position paper.
2. An Edmonton youngster was hospitalized yesterday after consuming a still-to-be-determined quantity of mothballs.
3. C
4. When you drop off your completed form, we will check to make sure that you have an up-to-date file.
5. Several drop-offs of over sixty feet make the Eagle Creek Trail a potentially dangerous one.
6. My grandparents left the mother country in 1908.
7. Listening to the rock group Rush, you would never think they were just a three-man band.

8. Many argue that abortion is not just a two- or three-sided question.
9. After two days of pitching and yawing on a fishing boat, I feel weak-kneed, windburned, and weather-beaten.
10. He decided his I-don't-care attitude was too easy; besides, it left him feeling empty.

Assignment 43B   Using Hyphens with Prefixes and Suffixes and with Fractions and Compound Numbers

Sample answers are provided below.

1. What number is the halfback wearing on his jersey?
2. I showed great self-control in the presence of those potato chips.
3. She has enjoyed her transcontinental railroad trip.
4. He answered the quasi-professional inquiry condescendingly.
5. The dancers' machinelike movements seemed odd to many in the audience.
6. We positioned the boat in midstream.
7. Cars need antifreeze to survive Saskatchewan winters.
8. Most of us recall our pre-adolescent years with mixed emotions.
9. The history of the post-Trudeau era is just beginning to be written.
10. The critics judged this novel to be a relatively unimportant work.
11. I finished about two-thirds of the test before time was called.
12. Four hundred and five thousand, two hundred and twenty-two spectators attended the game.
13. Over four thousand attended the concert last night.
14. The president-elect becomes president in a ceremony during our luncheon banquet next month.
15. She thought her pre-high school classes were the most difficult.

Assignment 43C   Using Correct Hyphenation

Incorrect hyphenations and their remedies are listed below.

1. C
2. *A frames* (A-frames)
3. *de-er* (deer)
4. *C-major* (C major)
5. C
6. *U pick* (U-pick)

226